P

h

pu

PICKING UP THE REINS

Also by Norman Moss

Men Who Play God: The Story of the H-Bomb and How the World Came to Live With It
A British-American Dictionary
The Pleasures of Deception
The Politics of Uranium
Klaus Fuchs: The Man Who Stole the Atom Bomb
Managing the Planet: The Politics of the New Millennium
Nineteen Weeks: Britain, America and the Fateful Summer of 1940

PICKING UP THE REINS

Norman Moss

Duckworth Overlook
London • New York • Woodstock

First published in 2008 by
Duckworth Overlook
90-93 Cowcross Street
London EC1M 6BF
Tel: 020 7490 7300
Fax: 020 7490 0080
info@duckworth-publishers.co.uk
www.ducknet.co.uk

A catalogue record for this book is available from the British Library

ISBN 978 07156 3693 0

Typeset by Ray Davies
Printed and bound in Great Britain by
Cromwell Press Ltd, Trowbridge, Wiltshire

For Jake Moss

Contents

"The reins of world leadership are slipping from Britain's competent but now very weak hands. These reins will be picked up either by the United States or Russia."

– Will Clayton, Asst. Secretary of State, May 1947

List of Illustrations

CHAPTER ONE

AFTER VICTORY

Rain was forecast in London for Saturday June 8, 1946 but dawn came bright and sunny, to the relief of people who were camped out overnight along the Mall, the broad avenue between Trafalgar Square and Buckingham Palace. Sitting on the sidewalk with their blankets and sandwiches and vacuum flasks of tea, they lined both sides of the avenue, beneath the tranquil willows of St James's Park on one side and the long straight walls and Doric pillars of the government buildings on the other. These walls were not gleaming white as they are today but grey and encrusted with grime like most buildings in London, the result of years of neglect, for the wartime struggle had left no room for niceties such as maintaining buildings. More people came to join the overnight campers and by ten o'clock the crowd was fourteen deep. People were gathered also along other streets all over central London, with mounting excitement.

They were waiting for the Victory Parade, for this was the day set aside to celebrate the end of the war ten months earlier, a national holiday. At mid-morning King George VI and Queen Elizabeth took their places on the reviewing stand in the Mall and the parade began.

The Mall has seen a lot of processions, the pageantry of the royal coach drawn by six black horses, the horsemen with their gleaming breastplates, the marching guardsmen in scarlet tunics, the fluttering flags. But this was not pageantry. The predominant color was khaki and the vehicles were not decorative. As Alan Moorehead wrote in the *Observer*: "Maybe some of the foreign representatives found it a bit dull. But in Britain and for the people of the empire who had suffered much and come a long way for this day, it had another quality: it was utterly and completely real. It was real to the point of grimness."

The leaders of the nation and the armed forces passed through the streets in open cars, Prime Minister Clement Attlee and Winston Churchill, the wartime premier, and then the generals and admirals, Field Marshal Lord Montgomery, always the showman, standing up in battledress.

Then the men and women who fought the war marched by, members of the armed forces and civilian workers also. The crowd cheered them all, including some with unfamiliar insignia: the Special Air Service, glider pilots, and the United States Marines, who had not been seen in Britain before. Troops from the empire marched too, Sikhs, Gurkhas, African soldiers. Allied troops followed, and there were loud cheers when the American detachment marched by, mingled with shouts of "Good on yer, Yank." Two-and-a-half million GIs had been stationed in Britain, and the sight of these Marines brought back memories.

Then came the vehicles, the tanks, troop carriers, trucks pulling artillery pieces, mobile canteens, and some unfamiliar monsters, like the flails, tanks with huge chains lashing about in front that cleared an area of mines. Civilians who had contributed to the war effort marched by, nurses, civil defense workers, and miners wearing their helmets. Land Army girls who had been drafted to work on farms, clad in their uniform khaki breeches, rode by on agricultural vehicles waving merrily. The marchers and the vehicles wound through the streets of central London and the crowd cheered them all, the applause prompted by gratitude.

The response was personal. The people watching from the sidewalk had been part of the war. In the years since then a mythology has grown up in Britain around the Second World War, epitomized in Churchill's oft-quoted phrase about 1940, "their finest hour," a story of a heroic nation standing together. Like most mythologies this has a large kernel of truth. The war was a collective experience for British people. Hardships and dangers were endured together, defeats and victories were felt together. In the years after the war many people expressed nostalgia for this feeling of unity, doubtless with memory undergoing its usual selective editing. "People are more selfish now. It's every person for himself. It was different during the war" – that kind of sentiment was heard often.

On that day in June memories were still fresh and vivid. The war had been literally close to home. When fighter planes, the Spitfires and Hurricanes, flew low overhead in formation, most of the people remembered seeing these aircraft in the skies above fighting German bombers, defending them in a way that was immediate and visible. When the big Royal Air Force bombers thundered over, people recalled seeing them take off into the darkness heading for Germany night after night.

There was a special cheer of gratitude when fire engines and other rescue vehicles drove by. *The Times* of London allowed its reporter an unusual rush of emotion at the sight of these. "It brought a queer pang to the heart, of mingled pride and pity, to think of vehicles like those of the rescue and fire fighting services, quietly manned and methodically working in a hell of bursting bomb and flame," he wrote.

Other cities had other memories. In Portsmouth and Southampton, there were parades along roads beside which, two years earlier, people had watched troop carriers and tanks rolling by on their way to invade France. In other south-coast harbor towns the celebrations recalled the spectacle of exhausted troops arriving back from Dunkirk in 1940, their evacuation across the Channel by a mixed Navy and civilian armada a triumph in a larger picture of defeat. For the war was a close-run thing. After the fall of France it had seemed likely that a weakly defended Britain would be Hitler's next conquest. As well as victory, the country was celebrating salvation.

There was a worrying absence among the Allied forces: no Soviet troops marched in the parade. The Soviet Union had declined an invitation to take part, and its absence aroused anxiety that the wartime alliance might change to rivalry. Had Red Army troops marched they would have been cheered as loudly as any. The predominant British attitude to Russia was gratitude. For a time it had been Britain's only ally in fighting Nazi Germany – admittedly a reluctant ally because it had not entered the war until it was invaded by Germany, but this was soon forgotten – and it was the first country to stop the apparently relentless progress of the Nazi war machine. The British people were aware that Russia had played the biggest part in defeating Germany, at tremendous sacrifice.

Two newly Communist countries, Poland and Yugoslavia, joined the Soviet Union in staying away. In what seemed like an attempt to appease Poland's new Communist government, the authorities had refused a place in the victory parade to representatives of the Polish Fifth Army. This had fought alongside the British and Americans in Italy and it owed allegiance to the anti-Communist Polish Government-in-Exile. Polish ex-servicemen were angry, and when members of the Polish squadrons in the RAF, which had played a key role in the Battle of Britain, were invited to take part they refused.

The Soviet army was still powerful and it was entrenched in the center of Europe. Other elements in the parade were a reminder of uncertainties in this new postwar world, for any who wanted to turn aside from the celebratory mood for the moment and contemplate them. The outlines of this world were not yet clear.

The Americans were marching with brisk confidence, but the American military were being withdrawn from Europe and from around the world. The United States alone possessed the most powerful weapon in the world in the atomic bomb, but it was in no mood to use either its power or its wealth abroad on a long term basis. The French troops who marched by represented a country divided by the war as Britain had been united, and uncertainty hung over its future. There was even more uncertainty about the future of Germany, already a problem at the heart of Europe. Men from Australia and New Zealand, who had come to fight for the mother country, marched by. But would their countries continue to look to Britain in the same way after seeing British power in the Far East smashed by Japan, to be restored only with American help?

The representatives of the Indian regiments evoked stirring images from British history, but that part of history would come to an end soon, for the British Government was pledged to give India independence. Colonial troops were a reminder that empires were in turmoil. There was rebellion against France in Indochina and against the Dutch in the East Indies, and stirrings elsewhere. The Malayan Chin Peng marched in the parade, honored for his part in leading a guerrilla war against the Japanese occupation. Eighteen months later he would be leading a Communist rebellion against British rule in Malaya.

The shabbiness of the buildings along the streets was a reminder of Britain's parlous economic state: The economic foundations of Britain's global power had been eroded by the war. How far they had been eroded was not apparent to those cheering from the sidewalk, nor indeed to anyone else at that time.

Soon the uncertainties hovering in the background would become stark and pressing. The crumbling of Britain's power and the near-collapse of the rest of Western Europe would open up a power vacuum into which the United States would move, not without hesitation.

One hundred and twenty years earlier a British Foreign Secretary, George Canning, the true begetter along with James Monroe of the Monroe Doctrine, said he had "called into existence the New World to redress the balance of the Old." Winston Churchill quoted these words in the Second World War, as American forces crossed the Atlantic to redress the balance on the side of Western democracy. Soon America would have to add its weight to the scales once again, with large-scale economic aid, with political muscle and then military support.

It would use its influence abroad as it never had before, first in Europe, then elsewhere in the world. The United States would become the pre-eminent world power, replacing Britain in its global role. This was something for which neither the American people nor the British were prepared.

There was much to celebrate. There were to be no more bombs falling on British cities, no more blackout, no more death rolls, and millions of families had their husbands and sons home safe. Peacetime had returned, but not peacetime normality.

Cities were drab. Night-time was dark. The wartime blackout was ended but neon signs and lighting in store windows were banned for reasons of economy. There was little sign of fresh paint. Rows of houses were interrupted by bombsites with weeds sprouting among the ruins, like cavities in a mouthful of teeth. Food, clothing, and fuel were rationed as tightly as they had been during the war. Housing was short, for bombing and neglect had taken their toll; one-tenth of British buildings were destroyed or damaged by bombs, and many returning servicemen began married life in their parents' spare room. Shopping for food meant standing in a queue and taking whatever you were offered when you got there. Every item of daily life, from pots and pans to furniture to clothes to whiskey, was in short supply.

Millicent King, raising two children alone in a village in Essex, wrote in her diary what many were thinking: "It doesn't seem fair that though the war is over, food is harder than ever to get, and with two hungry growing children to feed, it is exhausting finding enough food. With the twins' birthday coming up I've been trying to save luxuries like sugar and eggs to make a cake, but that means depriving them in the meantime." Whale meat made its appearance. Restaurant menus usually had a choice of two or three main courses, and often one of these was not available and portions were small. The American writer Edmund Wilson was taken by a friend to a first-class restaurant, where he ordered roast duck. "It consisted," he wrote, "of little dry and tough slivers from a bird that seemed incredibly thin for even a poorly fed barnyard owl." He was lucky to get that.

The countryside like the towns was littered with the detritus of war, rusting barbed wire, pillboxes and tank traps from the days in 1940 when Britain faced invasion and the whole country was a potential battlefield. Wartime airfields covered 240,000 acres and a drive was under way to turn them back into badly needed farmland.

The shortages were partly due to war damage, partly economic. For two centuries Britain had lived, as it does today, by importing food and other raw materials and paying for this from its overseas assets, and through exports and services. Now half its overseas assets had been sold off, including some large companies based in America and Argentina's railways. Shipping was a major money-earner and before the war the British merchant fleet had been the world's largest. Now a third of it was at the bottom of the ocean.

The British people felt proud of their country, proud that it alone had fought the war from beginning to end. The British way of doing things seemed validated by victory, just as, for many, the Soviet system seemed validated by its victory over Germany. If others pointed out illogicalities in British life, such as the hereditary House of Lords and the monetary system - twelve pence to a shilling, twenty shillings to a pound and a guinea was twenty-one shillings - Britons could say that these funny old ways had proved right for Britain. While other nations had caved in, they had prevailed. Muddling through had worked.

Although outright boasting would be out of character, they felt that both their behavior in the war and their policy of fair shares for all showed civic virtues lacking elsewhere. These days it is customary in Britain to compare one or another area of British life with that in other European countries - health services, transport, education, youthful attitudes - often to Britain's disadvantage. In those years few British people would suggest that Britain had anything to learn from its continental neighbors. There were two exceptions. It was generally accepted among thinking people that those in continental countries, particularly French and Italians, had better sex lives than the British and better cooking.

Britain then was a more class-stratified society than it is today. The landed aristocracy still had their wealth, although it had been eroded by two world wars, and they had political power as an element in the Conservative Party. The status of the upper class was institutionalized in "the season," the presentation of debutantes at Buckingham Palace followed by a round of private dances to launch them on to the marriage market. The middle class had expanded in recent years, and the professional middle classes still expected to have servants. Social surveys counted nearly two-thirds of the population as working class. Most of these worked in heavy industry, with nearly a million in coal mines, and they were easily identifiable by clothes, leisure pursuits, accents, and language - "thee" and "thou" were parts of speech among working-class people in the North. The royal family were respected and admired. It was felt that they had behaved well during the war, sticking it out with their people while many wealthy people had sent their children overseas to safety. Criticism of the royal family was rare.

The civic virtues of which the nation was proud were much in evidence. People waiting for buses formed orderly queues. Fair play was a supreme value. One man standing for Parliament in the 1945 election had a brother who was a convicted traitor because he had broadcast for the Nazis. His Labour opponent's campaign team decided that raising this as an issue would be unfair, and would be counter-productive because it would be seen to be unfair.

On that day in June there were hopeful signs. BBC Television, which began in 1936, five years before TV in America, went off the air when war broke out. Now it opened up again to televise the victory parade, albeit only to some 40,000 viewers in the London area who watched on their prewar sets. This seemed a harbinger of a return to peacetime. Prefabricated houses, small but serviceable mass-produced homes that looked like packing crates, designed to last five years, were going up in their thousands. The arts were flourishing: theaters and concerts had bigger audiences than ever, art galleries more visitors. In July the BBC started the Third Program devoted to classical music and the arts; today it is called Radio 3. Literary magazines flourished: *Horizon*, the *Times Literary Supplement*, *Penguin New Writing*. Despite rationing, people were healthier than they had been before the war and they lived longer. Everyone had jobs and children were given free orange juice and milk.

Eleven months earlier the British people had woken up one morning and found that they had elected the first Labour government in history (there had been coalition governments with a Labour majority for two brief periods). For most voters the Conservatives, despite the presence of Winston Churchill as their leader, represented the prewar days of the slump and the dole queue.

Americans were astonished by the rejection of the revered figure of Winston Churchill and many were alarmed by the arrival of a socialist government. When the warship taking President Truman home from the Potsdam Conference stopped briefly at Portsmouth harbor and he went on board HMS *Renown* to have lunch with King George VI (the nearest Truman came to visiting Britain) he said, "I hear you've had a revolution."

"Oh no," the King replied. "We don't have those here."

The 1945 election campaign was fought with passion. People cared about politics, and in those pre-television days they turned out in draughty halls all over the country to hear political speakers. The young Barbara Castle, later a cabinet minister, recalled campaigning in her constituency in Blackburn: "There was an unbelievable buoyancy in the atmosphere, as though people who had had all the Depression years, the men and women who had suffered in the forces, who had worked double shifts making munitions and the rest of it, suddenly thought, 'My heavens, we can win the peace for people like us.' That faith carried one along through all one's physical fatigue."

Hugh Dalton, the son of a chaplain to the royal family and a committed socialist who was to be Chancellor of the Exchequer in the new Government, wrote in his diary when the election results came in: "The first sensation, tingling and triumphant, was of a new society to be built, and we had the power to build it. There was exaltation among us, joy and hope, determination and confidence." Many who had voted for the Government shared this hope for a new society and celebrated the result joyfully. The result was a surprise, as was the size of the Labour majority, for the press had forecast a Conservative victory, and it brought gloom in some circles. On being told the news at a party at the Savoy Hotel a titled lady responded, "A Labour government? Nonsense! The country wouldn't stand for it."

The Labour Party then was a socialist party, committed in theory to "the public ownership of the means of production, distribution and exchange." It was a broad church, encompassing Marxists and liberals, ideologues and pragmatists. It was more of a class-based party than it is today. Although it drew support from all classes, its core membership were working-class activists, usually trade unionists, who aspired to rise with their class rather than out of it. Jack Jones, later the leader of the largest union, the Transport and General Workers' Union, was typical. Proud to be working class, he had fought for the Republic in the Spanish Civil War in the International Brigades, and he lived in a council flat. When he visited America he was shocked when an official of the Teamsters' Union took him to dinner at an expensive restaurant, and even more shocked when he told him that he owned it. The party's leadership was always shared between people who had come up through the ranks of the trade union struggle and middle-class believers who had entered politics from one of the professions.

The new Prime Minister, Clement Attlee, was one of the latter. He was a contrast to his predecessor as premier. Churchill was charismatic, eloquent, and volatile. Attlee was colorless, laconic, decisive, with a coldness that some found unnerving. A colleague, Christopher Mayhew, said of him, "He would never use one word where none would do." Unlike Churchill he was a good team player; he sought consensus in his cabinet. He was almost a caricature of the quiet, phlegmatic, pipe-smoking Englishman, his two passions cricket and the *Times* crossword. Yet his career, indeed his whole life, shows a passionate devotion to the cause of democratic socialism. As a newly qualified barrister, the product of a well-off home, public school, and Oxford, with a comfortable career in the law ahead of him, he went to help out at Toynbee Hall, a settlement in the East End of London. He was appalled by the poverty he saw there and impressed by the spirit of the people. With a small independent income, he dedicated himself full time to social work and to politics.

He was always a patriot. When war broke out in 1914 he was thirty-one but enlisted immediately (his brother Tom, a Christian Socialist, was a conscientious objector). He was wounded in the disastrous Gallipoli campaign and rose to the rank of major. He became a Member of Parliament in 1922 and leader of the Labour Party in 1935, and when Churchill formed his wartime coalition Government, as leader of the main opposition party he became deputy leader.

A new and fair society was the Labour Government's aim. The goal was inspiring but the path to it was cluttered with regulations and bureaucracy. A plethora of rules governed daily life, in the interests of fairness and also of the Government's plans for recovery. The Labour leaders believed in a planned, rational society. What upset them about prewar capitalist society, with its boom and bust and its mass of jobless, was not just its cruelty but its inefficiency. Resources, whether materials or manpower, should be used where they would do the most good, not deployed at some individual's whim or according to the requirements of the market, particularly at a time like this when resources were limited.

So civil servants decided, not only how the limited amount of food and clothing should be distributed, but where every other resource should go as well. Building materials would go where new houses or factories were most needed, fuel where it would most benefit society. Anyone in business had to fill out forms to get permission to buy supplies, hire staff, or rent premises. Every day brought some new instance of regulations being applied overzealously. A grocer was fined for selling a few extra pounds of potatoes even though they were frosty and would have gone bad if they had not been cooked at once, a tailor for using some spare scraps of material to make piping on a pajama jacket, a frivolity that was not allowed. The local council in Newquay, Cornwall applied to the Board of Trade for permission to buy sixteen cubic feet of wood to repair the boats in the children's boating pond and was told to apply to the Admiralty.

The national tone was moral earnestness. People were exhorted to work hard and pull together. A hundred thousand billboards went up saying: "We're up against it. We Work or Want – a challenge to British grit." The young Princess Elizabeth told a friend that the home of Queen Mary, the Queen Mother, was always freezing because she regarded it as her duty not to light coal fires. The Government produced a booklet called *Make-do and Mend,* showing a young woman holding up a stocking amid some pretty clothes that are presumably retreads. It advised Britons to cut old sheets in half down the worn middle, then sew the outside edges together so that the worn bits are now on the outside edge, and to make rugs and dolls out of rags.

People saved rubber bands and bits of string. Tinfoil was used and reused. Many people acquired habits of parsimony in those years that they retained for a lifetime.

Where there are more rules, there are more rules to break. These were the years of the spiv, the wide boy operating just the other side of the law, who could get you a bottle of brandy, lamb chops off the ration, or nylon stockings brought in from America, or find a tailor who did not ask for clothing coupons. The etymology of the word is uncertain. The best guess is that it comes from Romany, where *spiv* means a sparrow but also a smalltime crook. The war was over, men were not fighting and dying overseas, and it was difficult to persuade people that it was still their patriotic duty not to buy something on the black market if they could. One returning serviceman recalled years later: "Even persons of the utmost integrity, after six years of war, were motivated by self-preservation. It wasn't so much 'dog eat dog,' rather to make sure that no opportunity of easing one's existence was missed. I doubt if a single Englishman did not avail himself of the black market."

In September 1946 there was an exhibition at the Victoria and Albert Museum in London entitled "Britain Can Make It," showing the best products of British manufacturing: gleaming modern kitchen equipment, sleek new furniture, toys, telephones, women's clothes. It drew one-and-a-half million visitors. They might have looked admiringly at the exhibits but looking was all they could do. Most of the items on display were for export only or else had a long waiting list. Reflecting the nation's situation, King George, opening the exhibition, spoke of "our overseas markets, on which our solvency and standard of living depend." One can only imagine the reaction of his great-grandmother, Queen Victoria, if she had been asked to talk up the export trade.

There was something of a class-war atmosphere at this time. People took their politics into their professions, and there were societies of socialist doctors and socialist lawyers. It was not unknown for an employer to ask a potential employee his or her politics. Many among the wealthier classes took fright, exaggerating in their minds the revolution that was under way and hearing in the distance the sound of the tumbrels. Some emigrated, many to the East African colonies where servants were plentiful. Evelyn Waugh, whose novel *Brideshead Revisited* had just appeared as an elegy to a way of life that was passing, wrote in a characteristically dyspeptic diary note: "The French called the German occupying army 'the grey lice.' That is precisely how I regard the occupying army of the English socialist government."

Noël Coward, the court jester of the upper classes, entertained them with a song about their plight, "There Are Bad Times Just Around the Corner," with the concluding verse:

There are bad times just around the corner,
We can all look forward to despair,
It's as clear as crystal
From Bridlington to Bristol
That we can't save democracy and we don't much care.
If the Reds and the Pinks
Believe that England stinks
And that world revolution is bound to spread,
We'd better all learn the lyrics of the old 'Red Flag'
And wait until we drop down dead.

*

America provided a contrast to Britain. The United States alone among the combatant nations ended the war richer than it started. Its gross national product was more than double the prewar figure, $215.2 billion in 1945, against $101.4 billion in 1940. Manufacturing output had nearly trebled since 1939. The war had done what President Roosevelt's New Deal had failed to do and overcome the Depression. While Britain talked of "recovery," America talked of "reconversion," the conversion of the mighty industries that had poured out ships and tanks and aircraft and all the machines of war back to producing, now that they were safe from bombing, the machines of peace: cars and radios and household goods.

Some things were in short supply but compared to Britain the United States was a land of plenty, with brightly lit cities and crowds thronging restaurants and night clubs. One GI war bride from England arrived in America and was taken out to a restaurant for a welcome dinner with a family party of six. On being served a huge steak she assumed it was to be shared among the six of them, and was astonished to be told that it was one portion.

The Government could afford to be generous to veterans. Under the GI Bill of Rights these men could receive grants to pay the fees at college or training school, and more than two million took advantage of this. If they found difficulty adapting to civilian employment, an "adjustment allowance" of $20 a week, equivalent to a minimal salary in those days, allowed them to coast along for a year.

There were problems. Reconversion could not happen overnight. The nation was rich but the wealth was not distributed equally. Although corporate profits were at an all-time high, wages did not rise at the same rate. Rationing of food and petrol stopped when the war ended but price controls remained for a time. Farmers refused to slaughter cattle until they could sell at the price they wanted, so there was a shortage of meat. Money passed under the counter. A car dealer would sell a used car at the official price but only with an over-priced accessory. The National Union of Manufacturers complained about a "regulated economy." So Congress removed price controls, over the President's veto. Food prices rose by 50 percent. Wages did not keep pace and workers, freed from the wartime ban on labor stoppages, went on strike, on the railroads, on the docks, in the mines, in one industry after another. Five million people were out on strike at one time or another in the year after the war.

There were other disappointments. The war had been fought against Nazi racism but American society was racially segregated, by law in the Southern states, by practise in many areas of life elsewhere. Many Afro-Americans came back from the war, where they had served in segregated units, with new horizons and new ambitions, but they returned to the same restrictions that had cramped their lives before. In the South lynchings were one way of keeping Afro-Americans in their place. In Greensboro, South Carolina, a few weeks after the end of the war, sixteen people testified that they saw a gang lynch an Afro-American but a jury of the gang's townspeople acquitted them.

Yet even here things were getting better. Afro-Americans were now acceptable as sales clerks in smart stores. Herbert Sweatt challenged the University of Texas law school's refusal to admit him, beginning the long march to equal education. The next year Jackie Robinson would join the Brooklyn Dodgers and become a star player, breaching the segregation barrier in major league baseball.

In that first year after the war, more Americans married, more got divorced, more had babies. Some 3.5 million babies were born in 1946 against 2.7 million the year before. Benjamin Spock's book *Baby and Child Care* appeared and more Americans bought it than any book ever published except the Bible.

William Levitt, returning from a construction unit in the Navy, teamed up with his father, a property developer, and, using mass-production methods, started building houses in suburban Long Island which returning veterans could rent for $65 a month or buy for $8,000 with a $90 down-payment. This was Levittown, the first of many, and it began the American migration to the suburbs.

People felt good about their country. Their soldiers had liberated western Europe, welcomed with cheers by grateful peoples, and had humbled the

Japanese empire. American democracy as well as the American armed forces had triumphed. The most popular film of 1946, winning seven Oscars, was *The Best Years of Our Lives*, about three returning servicemen, all encountering problems but all facing the future with an optimism reflected in the title. The musicals of this time celebrated America: *Oklahoma!*, *Annie Get Your Gun*, *South Pacific*. To most, America was a land with promises to be fulfilled, the country to which the writer William Manchester returned from the Pacific war: "To the young veterans and their brides the late 1940s were easy years of exquisite laughter and lovers' vows, whose promise lingered like the incense burning in little golden vessels on the altar of the heart. To be young and not crippled was unbelievably lucky."

Americans had saved money during the war; and now they looked forward to spending it and to enjoying the fruits of their sacrifices, in a world in which the biggest problems had been solved. If there was one thing they feared, and there was, it was another depression. Images of the Depression were etched into the national memory: "Cox's army" of ex-soldiers camping in Washington to demand jobs; soup kitchens, bread lines, the hobo encampments ironically known as "Hoovervilles."

Everywhere there was a sense that a great evil had been defeated. Many sought something better than a return to prewar normality, looking for a way of life that was commensurate with the struggle and sacrifice of the war years. The young Arthur Miller was writing his play *All My Sons*, with its message about the responsibility we have for one another. In it a returned soldier reflects on the men in his company:

> They didn't die. They killed themselves for each other ... And I got an idea watching them go down. Everything was being destroyed but it seemed to me that one new thing was being made. A kind of responsibility. Man for man. And then I came home and it was incredible. I – there was no meaning in it here; the whole thing was a kind of bus accident. I went to work with Dad and that rat race again. I felt – what you said – ashamed somehow. Because nobody was changed at all. It seemed to make suckers out of a lot of guys. It felt wrong to be alive, to open a bank book, to drive the new car, to see the new refrigerator. I didn't want to take any of it.

This was fiction, one man's vision, but it was not only one man's. Here is the recollection of a prosperous insurance agent in Texas, reported by a social historian. Just out of the army he went to buy a car and the salesman wanted him to pay money under the table to evade price controls. "I told him to go to hell, that I had fought a war for decency and honesty and I wasn't going to be shaken down by some damned profiteer." He says he was angry and belligerent for a while, but he adjusted. "I still remember the bastards who thought the war was nothing more than a way of making money. I'm polite to them now and socialise with them and buy stuff from them. But I'll never respect them."

A new organization for veterans sprang up alongside the American Legion, which was nationalist and conservative, looking for something different and better. The American Veterans' Committee had a liberal approach; its slogan was "Citizens First, Veterans Second." Its organizer was Ralph Bolte, an American who had volunteered for the British Army and lost a leg in North Africa. It had 100,000 members, far fewer than the American Legion, but they were influential. When President Kennedy formed his cabinet in 1960, five members were AVC alumni.

Politically, this search for a less selfish world meant a search for a new international order looking beyond competing national sovereignties. If idealists found this desirable, many felt that the invention of the atomic bomb made it a necessity. The world was still taking in this new awesome power; after years of bombing campaigns by thousands of aircraft, here was one bomb carried by one aircraft that could destroy a city. The atom bomb seemed to make wars of the old kind impossible. More than that, it called into question the whole international order. *One World or None* was the title of a bestselling book of the time. This was a new world, and its structure was fluid and not yet set. Anything seemed possible.

Attlee contemplated a radical change in the international system. In September 1945, six weeks after the atom bombs were dropped, he wrote a long letter to Truman. "The world is facing entirely new conditions," he wrote. "If Mankind continues to make atomic bombs without changing the political relationship between states, sooner or later these bombs will be used for mutual annihilation." There is no record of Truman's reply.

The British Foreign Secretary, Ernest Bevin, followed this up with an appeal in Parliament that looked forward to the end or at least the diminution of sovereign nations. He would like to see, he said, "a world assembly elected directly from the people of the world as a whole, to whom the governments who form the United Nations are responsible." This was not empty rhetoric. Bevin concluded by telling the House of Commons, "I am willing to sit with anybody, of any party, of any nation, to try to devise a franchise or a constitution for a world assembly with a limited objective, the objective of peace." He sat down to shouts of approval from members who knew he meant every word of it.

In the US Congress, eighty-seven members of the House of Representatives sponsored a resolution calling for the United States to try to strengthen the newly founded United Nations and to "seek its development into a world federation." Gary Davis, who had flown as a US Air Force bombardier during the war, became an international figure when he threw away his passport and announced himself a citizen of the world, and invited others to follow. Passport-less, he traveled in Britain and France and was interviewed and commended. This postwar period was the high tide of liberal optimism.

Many thought the United Nations might supersede national sovereignty. An organization grew up in America called the United World Federalists, with the same aim of giving the UN supranational authority, of turning it, in effect, into a world government. The fulltime President of the United World Federalists was a young man, gifted and privileged, who exemplified these aspirations, Cord Meyer Jr. The son of a retired diplomat, Meyer was born into a wealthy background and attended private schools and Yale. At Yale he had a stellar academic record and played on the hockey team. With the war on he went from college into the Marines and was commissioned lieutenant.

The experience of battle determined the course of his life. He wrote to his parents from the Pacific island of Guam:

> As we buried our dead, I swore to myself that these deaths would not be forgotten or valued lightly. I felt more strongly than ever the wrongness of so many things. Their motionless young bodies, their inarticulate lips, seemed a monumental reproach to us the living, seeming to say, "Well, we did all you asked. We gave up everything, all we might have been and done, all love, all hope, all laughter, all tomorrows. What are you going to do now? Is it going to be any different, any better now?"

Shortly after this a Japanese hand-grenade exploded in his foxhole, leaving him with burns and shrapnel wounds and costing him his right eye. He was recovering in hospital in America when he received another blow: his twin brother Quentin, also a Marine officer, was killed on Okinawa.

Still in hospital, Meyer wrote in his diary: "The general notion of what I have to do is clear. I owe to those who fell beside me, and to the others who will die before this is done, the assurance that it is in my small power to make the future for which they died an improvement on the past ... The question is how? In what field of endeavor? Where to begin? Education? Politics? Writing?"

He joined the AVC and fought against attempts by Communists to gain control. Family connections had got him an introduction to the editor of the *Atlantic Monthly*. It published some of his letters home to his parents expressing his revulsion at war, and then an autobiographical short story about a

Marine fighting in the Pacific and his experience of being wounded, which won the O. Henry Prize in 1946 for the best story by a new writer.

He and another young ex-serviceman were invited to join the American delegation to the founding conference of the United Nations. Meyer argued that the founders of the United Nations had not gone far enough and that it should be given supranational powers, and this led him to the United World Federalists. He threw himself into his United World Federalists role, speaking and writing, including a book called *Peace or Anarchy*. He was a popular speaker on university campuses, sometimes speaking at seven in a week, a passionate figure with a handsome face despite his glass eye. "World government is possible. It is possible in our lifetime. We can and we will make it happen! By doing so we will achieve peace, not only for our children but for our children's children," he insisted, and young people stood up and applauded with hope in their hearts.

The damage caused by the war was both material and social and would take time to repair. When it was restored, the structures would be different from those that had been there before, and this applied to societies as well as cities.

The French Third Republic died with its defeat by Germany in 1940. General de Gaulle arrived with the liberating armies as the new President, and a constitutional assembly was set up in 1946 to devise a new constitution for a Fourth Republic. Italians voted to end their monarchy, making King Umberto II the last king of Italy, and the program was under way to devise a constitution for an Italian republic. In Germany government started from year zero, although there was a tradition of parliamentary democracy on which to draw.

In much of Europe the infrastructure, the railroads, bridges, roads, and fuel depots, had been systematically destroyed by air forces and armies. One-third of French railway tracks were out of commission and 95 percent of French canals were blocked. Food could not be moved about, nor materials to repair wrecked buildings. When the war ended, industrial production in France, Belgium and Holland was 30–40 percent of the prewar level; in Italy it was even less. The devastation and dislocation were so great that to anyone traveling around the continent today it seems unimaginable that such scenes existed within living memory. In April 1945, John J. McCloy, the US Assistant Secretary for War, wrote a report for the Administration from Germany saying: "There is complete economic, social and political collapse going on in Central Europe, the extent of which is unparalleled in history unless one goes back to the collapse of the Roman Empire, and even that may not have been as great an economic upheaval."

Sixty million people had been uprooted from their homes. The German lands of Silesia and East Prussia were handed over to Poland and seven million Germans fled or were expelled. Some escaped from East Prussia by sea which led to the worst maritime disaster of all time, the sinking by a Soviet submarine of the liner *Wilhelm Gustloff*, crammed with refugees; 7,800 people died in the icy Baltic waters. Three million ethnic Germans were expelled from Poland and Czechoslovakia, often with cruelty, for the war created savage hatreds. Many whose country had been freed by the Russians from Nazi occupation fled the Soviet version of liberation.

A new term entered the language: DP, or displaced person. There were more than a million DPs still in camps a year after the end of the war, kept alive by relief supplies. These included 125,000 Jewish survivors of the Holocaust, hoping for visas so that they could start a new life in another country.

The war had shattered old loyalties and given rise to new conflicts. For many the issues were not as simple as it seemed in America and Britain. Frenchmen under Nazi occupation had to choose between a legitimate government that had accepted defeat and made peace with Germany and a renegade government in a foreign country which refused to surrender. The Government-in-Exile was allied to Britain and America; most of the 50,000 French people killed in air raids were killed by British and American bombs. Some people in parts of the Soviet Union and the Baltic states joined the Nazis just to fight what they saw as their Communist occupiers, although many among them also welcomed the Nazis' persecution of Jews.

In the countries liberated from Nazi occupation there was a hunt for those who had collaborated with the Nazi occupiers which sometimes took the form of lynch law. Collaboration was a crime but it was a flexible term. Some people had collaborated with the enemy to better themselves, but some did so to help their fellow-citizens. Mikhail Gorbachev's village in the Caucasus was occupied by the Germans during the war. In his memoirs he tells how, when the village elder appointed by the Germans was imprisoned for treason after the war, the villagers protested that he had worked hard to protect them in his dealings with the Germans.

The occupation and the resistance legitimized law-breaking. In parts of the French countryside resistance fighters and some who just claimed to be took revenge on those who had collaborated with the Germans and for a time lawlessness reigned. Some resistance groups, with years of sacrifice behind them, were reluctant to yield authority in their areas to representatives of the Government. In Italy partisans fighting the German occupation formed the Committee for the Freedom of Northern Italy, which had a radical social program. They executed some 20,000 people as alleged fascists and collaborators including Mussolini, and took over some of their estates. In Belgium the Communists dominated the resistance, forming the Front d'Indépendance, and when the war ended resistance groups at first refused to hand over their weapons. The British moved tanks and troops into Brussels while the Government restored its authority.

The Belgian premier Paul-Henri Spaak reflected on the experience of occupation: "It had been the patriotic duty of everybody to oppose the government, to oppose authority, to do everything which it was your patriotic duty not to do. Suddenly to reverse it when the enemy was defeated, to get out of the way of lying and cheating, engaging in black market activities and all that – it was a tremendous moral crisis in our countries." *

Germany was destroyed as no nation has been destroyed in modern times, its cities pulverized, its infrastructure wrecked, its national morale wiped out. The German people had followed a leader who proved to be an evil fanatic and led them to disaster. They were a conquered people and their conquerors lived among them, in the occupying armies and the civil administrations, leading the privileged lives of conquerors and dictating the course of their lives.

In the Western occupation zones the official ration was 1,500 calories a day, but many people did not get as much as that. Today 3,000 calories is considered the minimum for an active person. People who had once led an orderly and comfortable existence lived in the ruins of buildings and begged Allied soldiers for cigarettes that they could trade for food. Professional men sought jobs in the kitchens of the occupying powers where leftovers were available. Some families survived only because one member was the girlfriend of an Allied soldier. There were desperate attempts at normality. A hairdressing salon kept open, but when a British officer's wife went for a shampoo she was told to bring a piece of wood or coal to heat the water.

Many among the occupiers felt as the American commander in Germany, General Lucius Clay, felt when he arrived in the ruins of Berlin: "I must confess that my exultation in victory was diminished as I watched this degradation of man." But there was little sympathy for German suffering. Two events shocked the world in 1945. One was the invention of the atomic bomb. The other was the discovery of the concentration camps and the Nazi gen-

* A Dutchman I know never forgave his father for obeying the law. When the German occupying authorities said that young men had to report for work in Germany, his friends went into hiding but his father would not countenance this. "We've always been a law-abiding family," he insisted, and took his son to the station to catch the train to Germany.

ocide of Jews, what later became known as the Holocaust. Today it is accepted as a fact of history, but then it seemed inconceivable, not something that anyone could do in the modern world. Yet the evidence was there, the numbing statistics illustrated by the newsreels of bulldozers pushing mounds of skeletal corpses into a pit.

One story related to the author shows just how unimaginable this was. It was told by a man who had been a doctor in the British Army during the war and was, incidentally, Jewish. He had been captured at the fall of Singapore in 1942 and spent the next three-and-a-half years in a Japanese prison camp, where, as he says, he received what he thought was a sound education in human cruelty. When he was released after the Japanese surrender, four months after the end of the war in Europe, the first newspaper he saw was a British Army paper, and this reported the finding of a commission that six million Jews had died in the Nazi extermination program. The headline contained a six followed by zeroes, and he said, "To this day I don't know whether it was a misprint or whether I had misread it, but I read the figure as 600,000." He was stunned. He knew about the Nazi persecution of Jews, but he could not believe that a Western nation could kill *six hundred thousand* people in cold blood. He went around for weeks trying to take this in. It was only when he talked to other people that he learned the true horror.

The Germans, having twice plunged Europe into war, were considered a race apart morally. Several theories were advanced as to why Germany's history had given it a propensity to embrace evil. A British film in 1947, *Frieda*, had the daring subject of a British soldier coming back with a German fiancée, and it was advertised on posters with the question "Would you allow Frieda into *your* home?" The writer and strategic thinker Herman Kahn, in a lecture, suggested several alternative metaphors for post-Nazi Germany as seen by others: the burned child, who has learned painfully never to play with fire; the cured rapist, who can be given parole but should be kept from temptation; the habitual criminal, who must always be watched closely.

The Western allies embarked on what was called de-Nazification, to purge public life of former Nazis, as well as putting on trial major and minor war criminals. There was a widespread feeling that as a people the Germans should be made to suffer in order to understand the evil they had inflicted. Behind the Allied occupation in its first phase was the spirit of the Morgenthau Plan, promulgated in 1943 by the US Treasury Secretary Henry Morgenthau. This called for the elimination of Germany as an industrial power and its reduction to a decentralized, largely agricultural country that would never again have the power to wage war. Such an impossible policy could only have been considered during wartime, reflecting hatred of the country which had inflicted such suffering on the world. It was made public, and the German propaganda machine used it as an incentive to the German people to fight to the bitter end.

Neither the American nor the British Government officially adopted it, but much of the occupation policy reflected its thinking. The official instructions for the American occupation zone declared that pending a decision by the Allied Control Council, "there was to be no production of iron, steel, chemicals, machine tools, radio and electrical equipment, automobiles and heavy machinery." It added that the occupation would be "a just, firm and aloof administration which would discourage any fraternization." Some American officials were even unwilling to repair the bridges across the River Main lest they be accused of "restoring Germany's war potential." The British zone, in northern Germany, encompassed the largest industrial concentration of all the zones. The Labour Government, with its socialist ideology, held the big German industrial corporations partly responsible for the war, and it set about nationalizing industry.

In fact, the Allies were sending food to Germany. Britain introduced bread rationing for the first time and cut its production of beer so that it could dispatch wheat and barley to its former enemy. Whatever people's feelings about Germany they were not going to let the German people starve. Attlee asked for American help in this effort, writing to Truman: "The ration there is already very low and substantial further cuts will bring starvation and unrest which, apart from humanitarian consideration, will increase our military commitments and retard Europe's recovery."

The Allies soon realized that they needed to get parts of the German economy going again so that the country would not be a burden on the occupying powers. They wanted to have the coal mines back in action to supply coal to the rest of Europe, as they had done in prewar days. One measure taken to increase coal production made economic sense but violated human instincts. To help them work effectively, miners were given special meals at their pithead canteens but they were searched as they left, to make sure that they ate the food themselves and did not take any home in their pockets to their hungry children.

Europeans, like Americans, wanted something better than a return to prewar conditions. The preferred engine of change was social democracy (where it was not Communism), which had a long tradition in Europe. So, politically, western Europe turned left. France, Italy, and Belgium were ruled by coalitions of parties ranging from the center leftwards, composed of Christian Democrats, Socialists and Communists. All these governments set in motion welfare programs and socially progressive measures.

The Communists had gained prestige in the war through the success of the Soviet army and through their role in the resistance movements. On V-E Day, 8 May 1945, John Bross, an American officer, drove from Paris to Biarritz and saw one village after another decked with red flags bearing the hammer and sickle, and he heard cries of "Vive Stalin!" In France and Italy women were given the vote for the first time and allowed to sit in parliament, and twenty-three women were elected to the French National Assembly.

In Asia also there was little wish to return to prewar conditions. The Dutch East Indies and French Indochina were in revolt against their colonial rulers. India and Malaya were swept by disturbances. There were uprisings against French rule in Algeria and on the Indian Ocean island of Madagascar, all of them put down brutally.

Most urgently, the world was short of food. Much of the great grain-producing areas of Europe were laid waste; Poland and the Ukraine, which used to export grain, had suffered two episodes of scorched-earth tactics, carried out first by the retreating Soviet Army and then by the retreating German Army. Farmers in those countries slaughtered their cattle because there was no grain to feed them. In France, Germany, Italy, and Belgium, crops were down nearly 50 percent. Even in Asia the rice crop was down 15 percent. The United Nations Relief and Rehabilitation Administration (UNRRA) saved many from starvation, in China, which received the largest amount of aid, Russia, Poland, and Greece, among other places. Among western European countries only Italy received UNRRA aid; the others, badly off though they were, had not reached starvation point. Edmund Wilson, who was disappointed with his sliver of bird in a London restaurant, ate at an outdoor restaurant in Rome and saw old people and children hovering, waiting for a chance to dart forward and snatch a morsel from his table.

America was the principal contributor to UNRRA and in addition the US Administration sent grain and dairy products to Europe. In February 1946 it issued a number of regulations to divert these foods from domestic consumption. Americans had less wheat in their bread, less grain for beer and whiskey, less cream for ice cream, and paid more for food so that some could be sent to Europe. Britain sent grain to Germany and to India, where famine ravaged Bengal. Aid to Europe was seen as a short-term measure, a leftover from the war. In those days foreign aid was not regarded as a normal function of government.

Government aid was supplemented by private generosity. Twenty-two organizations joined together to form CARE, the Cooperative for American Remittances to Europe. Individuals could pay for food parcels to send, starting at $10. There were also baby packages, containing nappies, blankets, powder, oil, and safety pins. Many children in Italy, Greece, France, and Germany kept rickets at bay because their families received CARE packages.

There was a fund of goodwill toward Britain in the US. For most Americans, wartime attitudes erased earlier images of British people as stiff-necked and imperious, typified by the redcoats that the American colonists had driven out. Most servicemen who had been stationed in Britain during the war came back with impressions of a friendly welcome and of a people enduring hardship with cheerfulness. American correspondents had reported back with admiration the determined behavior of ordinary British people during the bombing, and memories of this lingered. The broadcasts from Britain during the Blitz, particularly Ed Murrow's reports beginning "This is London …," were likewise still remembered.

The young Canadian actor Bernard Braden and his wife came to Britain after the war. "As we watched Londoners queuing everywhere," he recalled in his autobiography, "and going about their business in what appeared to be a state of apathy, we were acutely aware that they were the same people who had weathered the Blitz, displayed incredible personal bravery and had never given up. We watched them with a sense of awe." Even sixty years later, when New York City Mayor Rudy Giuliani visited London after the World Trade Center attack, he said, "People in London have always been remarkable. They were our inspiration on September 11th when we thought about how they reacted to the Blitz in 1940, and how they went through something far worse than we would ever have to go through."

This was not post World War One. The United States was not going to turn its back on the world and withdraw into isolationism. It was playing its part in the United Nations, and in the new international economic organizations that were intended to lay the foundations of global free trade. However, most Americans did not expect to be dealing with the world's problems. Roosevelt had told Churchill and Stalin that American troops would be withdrawn from Europe two years after the end of the war, and no one expected them to remain longer. He envisaged a world policed by the four great powers in concert, America, Russia, Britain, and China, under the aegis of the United Nations. China was assumed to be the China of the Nationalist Chiang Kai-shek or his legitimate successor. Roosevelt had been insistent that America would not take responsibility for European affairs after the war. On one occasion he wrote to Churchill: "Please don't ask me to keep any American forces in France. I just cannot do it! I denounce and protest the paternity of Belgium, France and Italy. You really ought to bring up and discipline your own children."

Twelve million Americans were in the armed services and seven million of them were stationed overseas when the war ended: American parents and their representatives in Congress wanted them home and out of uniform. "Bring the boys home" became an insistent demand. Under public and congressional pressure the Army, Navy and Air Force hurried to bring servicemen home and demobilize them, rapidly running down the strength of the services. Years later General George C. Marshall recalled this in a speech:

> I remember when I was Secretary of State, I was being pressured constantly, particularly when in Moscow, by radio message after radio message to give the Russians hell. When I got back I was getting the same message in relation to the Far East and China. At the time my facilities for giving them hell – and I am a soldier and I know something about the ability to give hell – was one and one-half divisions over the entire United States.

So far as most people were concerned, the outlines of the postwar world seemed clear. Despite signs of friction, the United States, Russia, and Britain would lead the United Nations in policing the world, preventing major conflicts. America's economic and military involvement in Europe was being brought to an end. It would continue to fund UNRRA for a little while longer until war damage was repaired and the countries of Europe and Asia got back on their feet. The occupation of Germany would be ended, foreign troops would be withdrawn, and there would be international arrangements to prevent Germany ever again becoming an aggressive power.

When the war ended Truman immediately cancelled Lend–Lease, the wartime program of military and other aid to allies, on the advice of his Director of the Foreign Economic Administration, Leo Crowley. He later admitted that he had not considered the implications. Crowley acted vigorously: he cancelled planned shipments immediately and even had ships carrying Lend–Lease material turned back.

This was a blow to Britain, for Lend–Lease was an essential part of its domestic financial arrangements. Attlee told an interviewer later, "It was a great shock. The tap was turned off at a moment's notice." It was a shock to the Soviet Union also. Realizing its mistake, the Administration allowed Britain to keep some Lend–Lease material or to buy it at knock-down prices.

The Labour Government's domestic program was ambitious. It set in motion welfare schemes and planned to nationalize key industries, the coal mines, gas, electricity, iron and steel. But the country's financial prospects were grim. Even to maintain the wartime standard of living Britain had to spend £1.1 billion a year on imports, but it was earning only £400 million from exports. It decided to turn to the United States for help, and in September 1945, a month after the end of the war and the cancellation of Lend–Lease, it sent Lord Keynes to Washington to ask for it. John Maynard Keynes was the pre-eminent economist of the time, his book *The General Theory of Employment, Interest and Money* the received wisdom on how a government should manage a national economy. He was confident that America would help with a grant, or at the least an interest-free loan. So far as he and the Government were concerned, America owed this to Britain. As Winston Churchill said earlier in the year, "We have given in the common cause, and may claim assistance from those we have helped to victory." They were to be disappointed.

Keynes took with him several arguments to demonstrate America's obligation. He showed that Britain's contribution to the war effort was disproportionately greater than America's in lives lost, resources spent, and civilian suffering. He showed that British deaths in the war totaled 450,000 against America's 418,000, with three times the population. (This figure included civilian deaths in air raids. If military deaths alone were counted America had more.) He calculated the contributions that Britain had made to US forces in one form or another at almost a billion pounds sterling plus other unquantifiable elements. But he found that his American opposite numbers were not responsive to these arguments. So far as they were concerned, America had already contributed enough to Britain's salvation. The best he could hope for was a loan. The negotiations went on for three months.

The two principals were ill matched and there was little meeting of minds. Keynes was a towering figure physically and intellectually, brilliant and arrogant, bisexual, married to a Russian ballerina, a member of the Bloomsbury set of intellectuals and aesthetes. His opposite number was Fred Vinson, a Kentucky congressman whom Truman had just appointed Secretary of the Treasury, and who was the President's poker-playing buddy and confidant. He was the kind of person the British ambassador, Lord Halifax, had in mind when he wrote in a dispatch soon after Truman became President of "the Missouri courthouse calibre of his entourage." To Keynes' eloquent expositions Vinson would respond, "Mebbe so, Lord Keynes, mebbe so. But down where I come from, folks don't look at things that way."

Keynes had more of a meeting of minds with the number two at the US Treasury, Harry Dexter White. White had learned his economics from

Keynes' texts and admired him, but he was not a man to be in awe of anyone and he argued with Keynes. He had always wanted to cut back Britain's system of imperial tariffs and he wanted to use the loan to advance this aim. The two men had met and argued before at the Bretton Woods conference to set up a postwar financial system. Later it was discovered that White had been a Soviet informant, if not actually an agent doing Soviet bidding.

Halifax sat in on the talks, and at one point a member of the British team penned a verse:

In Washington Lord Halifax
Whispered to Lord Keynes,
"They have the money
But we have the brains."

Cables flew back and forth across the Atlantic, the ones from London saying that the proposed terms were unacceptable, Keynes insisting, sometimes angrily, that they were the best that would be offered. He was suffering from heart disease and the strain told on him; he had a heart attack while he was in Washington. (He died six months later, aged sixty-two.) The negotiations went on until December.

In the end the loan was for $3.75 billion,* less than the $5 billion originally asked for, at 2 percent interest, to be repaid over fifty years. There were conditions: Britain had to open up imperial markets, and also abolish exchange controls and make the pound sterling convertible within a year of the first payments on the loan, a provision that worried Britain. The economist John Kenneth Galbraith called it "a formidable imposition of orthodoxy over common sense."

Canada also loaned Britain money, £1.5 billion, without onerous conditions, and this also helped alleviate Britain's plight.

The American loan still had to be approved by Congress, and this meant a battle. Conservatives like Ohio's Senator Robert Taft attacked it for "financing socialism," liberals like New York's Emmanuel Cellar for "bailing out British imperialism." One congressman asked why Britain should have to pay a lower interest rate than returning American servicemen trying to buy a home. Bernard Baruch, banker and presidential advisor, warned that if it gave the loan America might be shouldering too big a financial burden.

Fortuitously, Winston Churchill, a hero to most Americans, was visiting

* About $41 billion in today's money. According to the US Bureau of Labor's consumer price index, the value of the dollar then was roughly eleven times today's value. When other sums are mentioned in this book the reader can do her own arithmetic.

America and he assured Americans that the Attlee Government was not composed of "doctrinaire socialists" and that all British political parties stood four-square against Communism. Congressmen were persuaded that it was in America's interests to have a solvent Britain as an ally and trading partner.

Joseph Kennedy, a former ambassador to Britain and a leading Roman Catholic, testified on behalf of the Catholic hierarchy that Britain was a bastion against godless Communism and should be supported, and this was a powerful argument. Anti-Communism was to be deployed as an argument for aid to Europe again and again. Sam Rayburn, Speaker of the House of Representatives, spoke in a similar vein, "If we are not allied with the great British democracy," he said, "I fear somebody else will be. God help us when we have no ally across the Atlantic." After some debate both Houses ratified the loan in June 1946.

America saw the loan as generous, Britain saw it as niggardly. The battle in Parliament to get it accepted was almost as fierce as the battle in Congress, for many MPs resented the terms and wanted to reject the loan. One member accused the Government of "a cringing policy of appeasement." Leopold Amery, a passionate imperialist and one of those who always believed that America had designs on the British Empire, wrote that the terms were designed to break up the empire so that it would become "a field for American industrial exploration and in the end an American dependency." On the left Jennie Lee, a Labour MP, said: "There is no wisdom in this loan and there is no kindness in it."

But Attlee in the House of Commons and Keynes in the House of Lords insisted that, disagreeable as the terms might be, Britain had no choice but to accept them. This argument carried the day. But a number of Conservatives and Labour left-wingers voted against acceptance and there was a lot of bad feeling. The most bitter comment came in an editorial in the *Economist*, a journal not usually associated with anti-Americanism or with the left. "Our reward for losing a quarter of our national wealth in the common cause is to pay tribute for half a century to those who have been enriched by the war," it said. "Beggars cannot be choosers, but they can, by long tradition, put a curse on the ambitions of the rich."

The repayment period was to begin on December 31, which means that it would have ended at the close of 1996. In fact the period was later extended by ten years, so the final payment was made on December 31, 2006.

CHAPTER TWO

COMMUNISM AND COCA-COLA

So far as most British people were concerned, their country's economic weakness in 1946 was a glitch caused by the war, and would be repaired in time just as other war damage would be repaired. It was still one of the world's great powers, one of the Big Three along with the United States and the Soviet Union, the three countries that had parceled up the world at the summit conferences at Yalta and Potsdam in 1945. British atlases showed a quarter of the earth either ruled by Britain or linked to it in the Commonwealth. Britain ruled directly much of Asia and most of Africa and it was the dominant power in the Arab world.

British people were aware that their country was not as powerful or as wealthy as America, but they assumed that it played in the same league. Britain retained conscription, so its armed forces numbered 1.2 million. This was close to the size of the American armed forces, 1.4 million, and the United States had three times the population. Britain now had the largest army it had ever had in peacetime. Unlike most continental countries, where everyone did military service, Britain had never before had conscription in peacetime, apart from a few months on the eve of war in 1939. Historically Britain, like America, has had a libertarian dislike of a large standing army. It ruled a quarter of the world with a small army, but kept its imperial lifelines open with a powerful navy.

In October 1946 the British Government took a step in secret that demonstrated its intention that Britain should remain a great power: it decided to build its own atomic bomb. The background to this decision was an Anglo-American quarrel that arose partly out of a misunderstanding.

The wartime atomic bomb was an Anglo-American project. Small teams of scientists began work in both countries at the same time, but the Americans were not making much progress until exchanges of information began and they saw that the British were moving ahead. When it became clear that producing the bomb would be a major industrial enterprise that was beyond Britain's wartime capacity, British scientists went to America to join the much larger program there. In 1944, at Roosevelt's home in Hyde Park, New York,

Roosevelt and Churchill signed a secret aide-mémoire promising full cooperation after the war in atomic energy. Canada was also a party to this agreement because there was a laboratory in Montreal working on atomic energy and Canada supplied uranium. Later, at their meeting in Quebec, Roosevelt and Churchill agreed that neither party would use the atomic bomb without the consent of the other.

These agreements were so secret that neither Truman nor Congress knew about them. In 1946 Congress passed the McMahon Act, which established the Atomic Energy Commission as the body controlling atomic energy and atomic weapons, taking the matter out of the hands of the military. This act also forbade the passing of information to another country. So far as most Americans, and most congressmen, were concerned the atom bomb was an American creation; they knew very little about the British contribution. Attlee wanted further collaboration on atomic energy but the McMahon Act ruled it out, and in any case Truman was not interested. Senator McMahon said later that he would not have drawn up the bill as it was if he had known about the Hyde Park agreement.

Dean Acheson, the Assistant Secretary of State, learned about the Hyde Park agreement only in 1946 and his sense of integrity was offended by the blockage of information. "It was to disturb me for some years to come," he wrote later, "for with the knowledge came the belief that a Government, having made an agreement from which it gained immeasurably, was not keeping its word and performing its obligations."

Smarting at its rejection, the British Government established a cabinet committee to deal with atomic matters. The existence of this committee was secret. The Government had already set up an atomic energy research center at Harwell, in Oxfordshire, and it planned to develop nuclear power. In October 1946, the committee discussed the possibility of building a plant to produce fissile material for an atomic bomb. The two economics ministers, Chancellor of the Exchequer Hugh Dalton and Sir Stafford Cripps, President of the Board of Trade, insisted that the country could not afford it.

Sir Michael Perrin, a civil servant and one of the participants, recalled what happened next. The Foreign Secretary, Ernest Bevin, turned up after a long lunch, apologizing for being late, and Attlee summed up the view that Britain could not afford its own bomb program now. Bevin would not have this. "No, Prime Minister, that won't do at all," he said. "I don't mind for myself, but I don't want any other foreign secretary of this country being talked at, or to, by the Secretary of State in the United States as I have just been in my discussion with Mr Byrnes. We've got to have this thing over here whatever it costs." He ended by saying, "We've got to have a bloody Union Jack flying on top of it."

He won the day. The next month the Air Ministry put out specifications for a bomber to carry a 10,000lb bomb, and in May the following year Sir William Penney, who had been part of the team that built the wartime bomb, was instructed to design a warhead. Parliament was not told until a year later. This secrecy was a contrast to America, where questions concerning the atomic bomb were discussed widely and openly, and the scientists who had built the bomb played a part.

If the British public had known about the bomb program few would have objected. It seemed natural and proper that Britain, as a world power, should have any weapon that America possessed. Later, Attlee told an interviewer: "At that time nobody could be sure that the Americans would not revert to isolationism. There was no NATO then. For a power of our size and responsibilities, to turn its back on the bomb did not make sense." He was measuring British military power against that of a potential enemy. But Bevin was measuring it against America's power. He wanted it so that Britain could stand up to America, not Russia.

In fact cooperation with the United States was not entirely ruled out. A clause in the McMahon Act allowed for a limited exchange of information if it would contribute to the security of the United States. Furthermore, Britain, America, and Canada were still joined in the Combined Policy Committee which was to procure uranium jointly and share it out. British scientists were at the first postwar atomic bomb test at Bikini in April 1946 and helped assemble the bomb, but this was kept secret. Over the next years there were several British–American meetings to discuss nuclear weapons. The "consent" clause in the Quebec agreement was changed to "consult" and then removed. The Americans wanted to learn about British research into the effects of radiation, the British wanted help in testing nuclear weapons, which they did not get.

Some Americans did not want Britain to have the bomb, including Lewis Strauss, an influential member of the Atomic Energy Commission. Truman and Navy Secretary James Forrestal worried that in the event of war British nuclear facilities could be captured by the Russians. When this was put to the British, Sir Roger Makins, who was heading the British side, said, "Any suggestion that valuables were not safe in this island is one we are not prepared to admit."

The talks were carried on in secret but the Russians were well informed. The official at the British Embassy in Washington taking part was Donald

Maclean, who was later revealed to be a KGB agent. There was cooperation in the purchase of uranium and in marginal areas but not in the design of weapons. At the end of one series of meetings, in December 1948, the then British ambassador, Sir Oliver Franks, cabled home: "The whole question of our relations with the Americans on the atomic energy question seems to be bound up with the larger issue of the extent to which the Americans are prepared to treat us as a first-class power."

Bevin's interjection in the discussion on an atomic bomb followed by his victory over his cabinet colleagues' views was typical of the man in both substance and style. He thought Britain should remain a great power and the world would be better off if it were. Attlee's government was cabinet government. Ministers were expected to be responsible for policy in their own departments. Bevin had an unusually free hand in creating British foreign policy. Attlee said once, "You don't keep a dog and bark yourself, and Ernie is a very good dog." Bevin pursued policies that were independent of Attlee's views and in some cases in opposition to them, and Attlee allowed himself to be overruled.

Ernest Bevin, a large, thick-set man, was a working-class trade unionist with no formal education. He was the illegitimate son of a farm worker who left school at fourteen to drive a drayman's horse and cart, then became a union activist and educated himself in history and politics. He became the leader of Britain's largest union, the Transport and General Workers' Union, and Churchill brought him into his wartime cabinet as Minister of Labor to keep labor behind the war effort. This is not a likely background for a successor to the great foreign secretaries who wielded power in the days of Britain's imperial greatness. Yet at a time when Britain's global reach was declining, Bevin had as much influence in the world as any of them, shaping events and institutions with far-reaching effects. He was one of the architects of the postwar world.

Although his appointment was a surprise Bevin had always had an international viewpoint. He wore all his life a signet ring given to him by the American labor leader Samuel Gompers when he was with a British delegation to an American union conference in 1915, and whenever he visited America as Foreign Secretary he talked to labor leaders he knew. In 1919 he organized a strike of dockers to halt the shipment of weapons to the White Russian forces in the Russian Civil War, and he was an early champion of European unity. He came to office with no fixed set of policies, and came round only reluctantly to accept a world in which Communism and the West were competing power blocs.

In the group photograph of Attlee's government, thirty-four sober-looking men in dark suits, white shirts and ties and one woman sit looking at the camera. Bevin sits in the front row next to Attlee, his large hands on his knees, taking up nearly twice as much room as most of the others, a stone monument of a figure. In a country with a highly developed sense of class distinction, Bevin was a natural democrat. At an official dinner once, he talked to the wife of a senior civil servant and found that she came from Bristol, where he had once worked. Pursuing this they found that he had at one time delivered laundry to her house. He saw this as a point of commonality, the difference in their status at the time unimportant. He was at ease among the Oxford- and Cambridge-educated mandarins of the Foreign Office, despite his working-class accent, his dropped aitches and slight West Country burr. He called the permanent under-secretary at the Foreign Office, Sir William Strang, "Bill," the only person who would dare do so or would be allowed to.

His instincts are seen in an exchange with Chaim Weizmann, the Zionist leader, about anti-British terrorism in Palestine. Bevin said, "I can't bear English Tommies being killed. They are innocent." Weizmann pointed out that millions of Jews had been killed by the Nazis and some were dying still in refugee camps. Bevin said, "I don't want Jews to be killed either, but I love the British soldiers. They are my people. They are working class."

He had little time for abstract conceptualizing, but he would ruminate about a situation and listen to opinions. He was a poor sleeper and would often wake at five o'clock in the morning, make himself a cup of tea, and read official papers, and then go into the office in the morning with a decision. He was implacable to opponents. If he arrived at a policy it would be "my policy" and a critic was an enemy. When someone remarked of Aneurin Bevan, the brilliant, mercurial, and sometimes impulsive Health Minister who had often quarreled with Bevin, "Aneurin is his own worst enemy," Bevin growled, "Not while I'm alive he ain't."

Yet, for all Bevin's belligerence, his years as a trade unionist had given him skill and understanding as a negotiator which Foreign Office officials recognized. As Lord Strang wrote, "He understood that the aim of negotiation is not outright victory but an acceptable outcome."

Ideologically, the Labour Party was anti-imperialist: it believed in principle that people should govern themselves. It was setting out to give independence to India. However, it seemed that most colonies were not yet ready to govern themselves, and the Labour Government brought to British rule the same zeal for planning and humane concerns that it demonstrated at home.

Bevin told the cabinet in August 1945, talking about territories in the Middle East: "I am anxious to promote schemes of economic development which would benefit the common people. Perhaps also we might contribute to the welfare of Middle Eastern countries by supplying them with medical services." Again and again when he talked in cabinet about the Middle East, he returned to this theme: he wanted British policy to benefit the mass of the people, not only the "princes and pashas," as he called them, who were Britain's principal allies in the region.

The Government recruited more colonial officers - in 1947, twice the prewar annual figure. It had ambitious plans for exploiting natural resources in the African colonies for the benefit of both native populations and Britain, displaying the same kind of optimism about economic planning it was displaying in domestic affairs. Officials held exaggerated expectations. The Government poured money into a groundnuts scheme in Tanganyika (now Malawi) which failed. At one point Bevin said to Dalton: "If we only pushed on and developed Africa, we could have the US dependent on us and eating out of our hand in four or five years," a remark which reflected the resentment of American power that occasionally surfaced in almost everyone in Britain.

Attlee retained for longer than Bevin the hopes of continuing cooperation with the Soviet Union in the postwar world. He was worried about imperial overstretch. He rejected the traditional Foreign Office view that a dominant position in the Mediterranean was vital for Britain as the route to its Asian empire, and he was prepared to pull out of that region. At this time Britain was supporting, with both men and money, the Greek Government in its civil war against the Communists and it had bases in several Middle Eastern countries. Attlee wrote in a memo:

> I do not think the countries bordering on Soviet Russia's zone viz, Greece, Turkey, Iraq and Persia can be made strong enough to form an effective barrier. We do not command the resources to make them so. If it were possible to reach an agreement with Russia that we should both disinterest ourselves as far as possible in them so that they become a neutral zone, it would be much to our advantage. Of course it is difficult to tell how far Russian policy is dictated by expansionism and how far by fear of attack by the U.S. and ourselves. Fantastic as this is, it may be the real ground for Russian policy.

Bevin, unlike Attlee, had come to see Russia as a potential aggressor. "If we evacuate the area, we make a gift to Russia of the manpower of the region and the oil," he argued. "This would make a difference of 100 millions in the balance sheet, and possibly a great difference in our dollar earnings ... It would be Munich all over again, with Greece, Turkey and Persia as the first victims in place of Czechoslovakia. Furthermore, America would write us off." Bevin may have wanted to improve the lot of people in the Middle East but he was also going to look after Britain's interests. He told a Labour Party conference in 1947: "We cannot afford to lose our position in the Middle East. Our navy, our shipping, a great deal of the motive power for our industry in the shape of oil are there. The standard of life and the wages of workmen in this country are dependent on those things."

The Greek commitment began while the war was still on. The main resistance to the German occupation in Greece was provided by ELAS, a guerrilla army that was led by Communists. When the Germans and Italians pulled out as the war ended ELAS controlled much of the countryside and tried to seize power in Athens. British troops landed, suppressed ELAS, and ensured that the Greek king, who had been in exile in London, could return to power. Most American commentators saw this as Britain installing an unpopular royalist regime. The US Secretary of State, Edward Stettinius, said the liberated peoples of Europe should work out their future for themselves, which was taken as criticism of British policy in Greece.

A truce was arranged, but moves toward a government that would include the Communists broke down, and civil war ensued. Many who had fought in the resistance were accused of being Communist and were driven into ELAS by harassment and killings. ELAS was not a tightly organized, centrally controlled force and most of its members were not members of the Communist Party. In the countryside, where most of the war was taking place, a quarter of the people were illiterate. In the mountains that cover most of the country, bands of men under their local leaders who had fought the Germans now fought a guerrilla war against their own Government's army.

British troops trained and supported the Greek Army and the British Treasury financed it. It was a cruel war. British and later American advisors tried to limit some of the repressive behavior of government forces. A Foreign Office memo warned that if foreign support were withdrawn the Government would collapse and people would turn to a General Zervas. He, the document said, "would no doubt proceed to measures of the utmost ruthlessness, unchecked by the necessity to have regard for the susceptibilities of British and American public opinion." However, the royalist Greek Government was corrupt. With the country on the edge of starvation it was the biggest European recipient of UNRRA aid, but much of this produce ended up on the black market, sold for the benefit of Greek politicians and their friends.

Moreover, many of the Government's supporters had collaborated with the Nazi occupation. Nonetheless, a referendum declared by international observers as having been fairly conducted showed a majority supporting the Government.

This reactionary Greek Government was unpopular in Britain, particularly in the Labour Party. One left-winger, Tom Driberg, said that the civil war was a struggle between "the bulk of the Greek people on one side and quislings and royalists on the other backed by British bayonets." Attlee himself was having doubts. In December 1946 he wrote in a memo to Bevin, who was then at the United Nations in New York: "I am beginning to wonder whether the Greek game is worth the candle."

It was another country in the eastern Mediterranean that was producing the angriest disagreements between Britain and America at this time: Palestine. Britain had governed Palestine since the end of World War One. In 1917 the British Foreign Secretary, Arthur Balfour, announced that Britain supported a Jewish national home there, without prejudice to the rights of the existing population. This was like promising a national home for cats without prejudice to the rights of the existing population of mice, although in Palestine who were the cats and who were the mice would be disputed by the parties involved.

Jewish immigration increased in the 1930s, spurred by the Nazi persecution, and so did violent resistance by Arabs. Arab nations rallied to the support of the Arabs in Palestine. In 1939, to appease the Arabs, Britain limited Jewish immigration, just at the time when Nazi persecution was intensifying. With a militarily hard-pressed Britain facing war with Germany this made sense, but the refusal of a haven to German Jews condemned many to death. The response in Palestine was the growth of Jewish underground organizations which fought the British. After the war the restrictions on immigration remained and the underground war against the British continued. In the wake of the Holocaust world opinion was sympathetic to the Jews, among liberals in particular. European Jews had suffered like no other people in modern times. In Palestine they were bent on establishing a modern democracy in a land surrounded by Arab dictatorships. The case of the Palestinian Arabs, who saw much of their homeland being taken over, was rarely heard.

Truman was personally sympathetic to the Jewish case on Palestine, but the strong Jewish presence in American political life in any case made it incumbent upon him to support it. In October 1946, with congressional and many gubernatorial elections due the following month, the Democrats were worried about New York, where Thomas Dewey was the Republican

Governor standing for re-election. New York State Democrats told Truman that Dewey was about to issue a statement calling for the admission of more Jews to Palestine and they asked Truman to pre-empt this. Truman said he would.

His Secretary of State, James Byrnes, warned Attlee that this was coming. Attlee asked Truman to delay it for a few days because he was in delicate negotiations with Jews and Arabs, trying to arrange at least a temporary agreement. But Truman went ahead and on Yom Kippur, the Jewish holy day, he called for the admission of 100,000 Jews to Palestine immediately. Attlee was furious, and Bevin denounced the move in Parliament, pounding the dispatch box angrily and saying, "I cannot be expected to carry on negotiations under the handicap of American local politics!" This was greeted with cheers from all sides.

The Foreign Office was looking at Palestine in the context of its position in the Middle East. A briefing paper for officials attending a meeting in Washington said: "The Americans must realize that their continued support for Zionism has an extremely serious effect on the readiness of the Arab world to co-operate with us, and that without their co-operation our strategic hold on the Middle East will be much more difficult to maintain." The State Department did realize this. A group of American Middle East diplomats went to Truman and warned him that his stand was damaging America's interests in the Arab world. He was frank in his reply. "I'm sorry, gentlemen," he told them, "but I have to answer to hundreds of thousands who are anxious for the success of Zionism. I do not have hundreds of thousands of Arabs among my constituents."

Zionists were trying to smuggle Jews from Europe into Palestine and the British Navy was intercepting them, a drama that was enacted before the world's press. Most American newspapers portrayed the British as oppressors and the Jews in Palestine as their victims. The popular columnist Walter Winchell customarily referred to "the Brutish." When Congress was debating the loan for Britain, congressmen with heavily Jewish constituencies were being urged by their constituents to vote against it.

Bevin was attacked in America for telling a Labour Party conference that Americans wanted Jews in Palestine because "they don't want too many Jews in New York." This was undiplomatic but he had some ground for his cynicism. Congressmen were falling over each other to express sympathy for Holocaust survivors but they would not ease the immigration quotas to allow more of them entry to the United States. A Gallup poll showed that they would have been opposed by most Americans if they had.

Truman was ill prepared for the responsibilities that were thrust upon him with the sudden death of President Roosevelt in April 1945, just eighty-two days into Roosevelt's fourth term. He had not been a part of the President's inner circle and had not been privy to the great decisions that were taken. He did not even know about the atom bomb project that was then nearing completion. He had little experience of international affairs and had never been abroad apart from his army service in France in World War One. Since Roosevelt must have known what everyone close to him knew, that he was a sick man and that it was very possible that he would not complete his term of office, keeping his vice-president out of the policy-making loop seems irresponsible.

Harry S. Truman – the "S" was an initial he added when he was young; he had no middle name – was the most ordinary man to occupy the White House in the twentieth century. He went into local politics in Missouri after an unsuccessful career first as a wheat farmer and then as a menswear storekeeper. He acquired a well-deserved reputation for scrupulous honesty, which was remarkable because he owed his start in politics to the crooked Pendergast machine in Kansas City. He gained national fame as the head of a Senate committee investigating waste and profiteering in war spending, and was chosen as vice-presidential candidate in 1944 because the incumbent, Henry Wallace, was regarded as too left-wing and too flaky. Truman supported Roosevelt's New Deal policies on the ground that they helped the little man, but he had little time for some of the intellectuals in Roosevelt's circle and for what he called "professional liberals."

He was most at home with his old Missouri friends or a few Southern colleagues in the Senate, playing poker, drinking bourbon and water, swapping down-home stories. He had no education beyond high school but he read widely in history. According to his own account he could not do sports when he was young because he was short-sighted, so he read a lot; he claimed to have read every book in the public library in Independence, his home town. His knowledge was wide rather than deep. When the eastern Mediterranean was being discussed, he would cite the campaigns of Alexander the Great. His view of situations was rarely nuanced: he tended to see international affairs in black and white terms. Countries were either dictatorships or they were not; leaders either kept their word or they did not. He believed in democracy and in the good sense of the mass of the people. He was rarely subtle in thought or speech. Roosevelt was charming and circumlocutory, Truman was brusque and decisive. Roosevelt was an inspiring orator. Truman was direct and could be persuasive, but he was never eloquent

In the White House he would go for a brisk walk early most mornings, dressed neatly in a double-breasted suit, white shirt and bow tie, accompanied by secret service agents. People would call out asking how he was, and he would reply, "Just dandy."

He had few vices; he saw the Folies Bergère in Paris as a young soldier and thought it was "disgusting." But he could lose his temper and would explode into violent and often juvenile language, sometimes in writing. Reflecting the worldview of many ordinary Americans at the time, he once, in a letter to his wife Bess, conflated Communists, leftists, bohemians, cranks, fascists, and sexual deviants. "The attempt of Lenin, Trotsky, Stalin et al., to fool the world and the American Crackpots Association represented by Jos. Davies, Henry Wallace, Claude Pepper and the actors and artists in immoral Greenwich Village is just like Hitler's and Mussolini's so-called Socialist states," he wrote.

He was impulsive. When he wrote to Henry Wallace demanding that he resign as Secretary of Commerce the letter was violent and contained profanities. Wallace, decently concerned for the dignity of the presidency, agreed with one of Truman's aides to burn the letter, and Truman wrote another. On another occasion, when he was in the White House, Truman wrote an angry letter to Bess, back home in Independence, then had second thoughts and had the postmaster in Independence intercept the letter and destroy it. Usually, he restricted his intemperate language to his diary and his letters to Bess, but sometimes it slipped the boundaries. When the *Washington Post* music critic slated a concert performance of songs by his daughter Margaret, he wrote him an abusive letter which ended, "Some day I hope to meet you. When that happens you'll need a new nose, a lot of beef steak for black eyes, and perhaps a supporter below!" The letter was made public.

However, he rose to the demands of his office. He believed in American ideals. He saw the great international challenges for what they were and, if he expressed them in simple terms of good and evil, that was the way most Americans were able to grasp them. He even overcame his upbringing in the racist atmosphere of the segregated South to fight for civil rights.

Domestically, his presidency was a continuation of Roosevelt's. In his first State of the Union address he called for an extension of welfare measures and fair employment laws. In international affairs the overriding question was relations between the West and the Soviet Union. Some in Roosevelt's Administration had had high hopes of continuing the wartime alliance, and the founding of the United Nations seemed to show promise.

Roosevelt and Churchill had virtually handed over Poland and the Baltic states to Stalin when the Big Three met at Yalta, in the Crimea, in February

1945, and agreed on the postwar boundaries of Europe. This was acquiescing in a *fait accompli* because Soviet armies were already occupying most of Poland and were reoccupying the Baltic states. People in government in London and Washington were sympathetic to the Soviet desire for a friendly government in Poland. They were aware of the terrible devastation caused to Russia twice in the century by invasions through Poland. Yet it was becoming clear that Russia wanted a Polish government that was not only friendly but subservient. It had promised free elections, only to install a government dominated by Communists.

In the countries in eastern Europe that the Soviet armies occupied they established coalition governments including Communists, and allowed free elections. But in every case the situation was to be transformed by stages into a Communist dictatorship. In Hungary the Soviet Union, which was still in occupation, accused the governing Smallholders' Party of subversion and arrested its leader, prompting the Prime Minister to flee. In Romania this takeover by stages resulted at one point in the bizarre situation of King Carol presiding over a Communist government, until he was allowed to abdicate. In Bulgaria the transformation was perfunctory. Yugoslavia was a special case. There Communists had seized power without Soviet help after a partisan war against the German occupiers.

In the early postwar period, the Soviet Union seemed more hostile to Britain than to the United States. Britain was an imperial power and areas where it held sway touched on the Soviet borders, particularly in the Balkans and the Middle East. At the Yalta conference a State Department paper warned of "the growing evidence of Anglo-Soviet rivalry in Europe, and the resulting power politics scramble for position." Another State Department memo in October 1944 said the United States might have to play the role of mediator between Britain and the Soviet Union, given "the absence of any conflict of vital interests between the United States and the USSR ... and the number of points at which the British and Soviet interests impinge." *Pravda*, the official Soviet newspaper, often attacked Britain and disputed the claim that the British Government was in any way socialist. It did not want European workers seduced away from the Soviet road to socialism. So far as Communists were concerned, British Conservatives were the class enemy, but the Labour Party leaders were class traitors.

Walter Lippmann, the preeminent American commentator on foreign affairs, wrote in his column: "Anglo-Soviet difficulties extend in a wide arc through the Balkans to the Middle East and Persia. If ever there was a time when a wise reserve was called for on our part, it is now." Americans were quite ready to maintain reserve about any disputes Russia had with Britain. So far as they were concerned, this was one more quarrel between European countries and they did not see any need to get involved.

The Foreign Office, like the State Department, was divided on its attitude to Russia, but Foreign Office officials were coming to see Russia as a hostile power and were worried that the United States did not take the same view. Halifax complained in a cable from Washington in December 1945: "There is a stubborn determination in responsible quarters here to rationalize the actions of the Soviet Union wherever possible and to make conciliatory words if and when the opportunity presents itself."

While Parliament was still expressing friendly sentiments, the Foreign Office set up a department to wage propaganda warfare against the Soviet Union called the Information Research Department. It responded to the establishment of the World Federation of Democratic Youth, which was dominated by delegations from the Soviet Union and their sympathizers, by sponsoring a rival World Assembly of Youth, keeping its connection with it secret. It monitored domestic Communist influence. Later it created a comic-strip version of George Orwell's anti-Soviet satire *Animal Farm*, and offered his dystopian novel *Nineteen Eighty-Four* free of charge to foreign publishers. The BBC World Service began broadcasting in Russian in 1946, a year before the Voice of America.

The British Secret Intelligence Service began conducting covert operations against the Soviet Union, landing agents and resistance groups recruited from among anti-Soviet refugees on the coasts of the Baltic states. This continued a campaign which the service had been waging in the 1930s but which had been halted during the war on Churchill's instructions. Several of these agents were caught, so Russia knew about these operations. When the Soviet Government talked of Western hostility, it had some reason.

In March 1946 Winston Churchill, then leader of the Conservative Party Opposition, visited America and addressed an audience at the small Westminster College in Fulton, in Truman's home state of Missouri. With Truman sitting beside him on the platform, he made a speech in which, as he had done before, he introduced a phrase into the language. "From Stettin in the Baltic to Trieste in the Adriatic," he said, "an iron curtain has descended across the Continent. Behind that line lie all the capitals of the ancient states of central and eastern Europe." He went on to speak of the danger that Communist parties around the world presented.

His phrase "iron curtain" is known and remembered. What is not so well remembered is that in the same speech he introduced another phrase into the language, one that has been heard in the years since then in Britain more often than in America. He said that what was needed to meet this new barrier was "a special relationship between the British Commonwealth and Empire and the United States." He went on to spell out what he envisaged:

> Not only the growing friendship and mutual understanding between our two vast but kindred systems of society, but the continuance of the intimate relationship between our military advisors, leading to common study of potential dangers, the similarity of weapons and manuals of instructions, and to the interchange of officers and cadets at technical colleges. It should carry with it the continuance of the present facilities for mutual security by the joint use of all Naval and Air Force bases in the possession of either country all over the world.

The speech created anxiety in America. Commentators warned against being dragged into Britain's quarrels. Walter Lippmann criticized Truman for applauding it and wrote: "The line of British imperial interest and the line of American vital interest are not to be regarded as identical." Truman said he had not known in advance what Churchill was going to say. (This was not true; he had read the speech on the train from Washington.) Secretary of State James Byrnes assured Americans: "We have no more intention of forming an alliance with Britain against Russia than we have of forming an alliance with Russia against Britain." The *Wall Street Journal* summed up the response: "The country's reaction to Mr. Churchill's speech must be convincing proof that the United States wants no alliance or anything resembling an alliance with any other nation, at least one outside the American continent."

Evidently, Churchill had gone further than many Americans were prepared to go at that time in depicting an implacably aggressive Soviet Union, and much further in summoning up the picture of a new Anglo-American alliance to confront it. The marriage proposal was rejected.

Under Roosevelt foreign policy had been made in the White House, sometimes capriciously. Although Truman would sometimes refer to diplomats, in American demotic, as "cookie pushers" and "the striped pants boys," he was ready to turn to the State Department for advice and to let it play its role.

Roosevelt had high hopes of good relations with the Soviet Union after the war, although in the last months of his life he was coming to have doubts about this. In his first days in office Truman read the text of the Yalta agreements and held meetings with senior advisors about relations with the Soviet Union. Eleven days after he took office he met Soviet Foreign Minister

Vyacheslav Molotov when Molotov was on his way back from the founding conference of the United Nations in San Francisco. He berated the Soviet Union in blunt, undiplomatic language for not allowing free elections in Poland. Molotov, outraged, said, "I've never been talked to like that before in my life." Truman said, "Carry out your agreements and you won't get talked to like that." When Molotov tried to argue, Truman dismissed him with the words, "I would appreciate it if you would transmit my views to Marshal Stalin."

Truman's interpreter at the meeting was Charles Bohlen, one of the group of Soviet experts in the State Department whose views had been ignored by the Roosevelt White House, which took a more positive view of the Soviet Union, particularly during the war years. Bohlen wrote in his memoirs that he had enjoyed translating Truman's words, and that "they were probably the first sharp words uttered during the war by an American president to a high Soviet official."

However, Truman had second thoughts. He told Joseph Davies, a former ambassador to Russia, that he had given Molotov "the old one-two to the jaw." Then he asked anxiously, "Did I do right?" He was worried about alienating the Soviet Union. For one thing, the Pacific war was still on and America wanted Soviet participation. On the advice of some old Russia hands he asked Harry Hopkins to go to Moscow and assure Stalin that he desired cooperation and a lasting peace. Hopkins was one of the New Deal figures who had been most sympathetic to the Soviet Union in the past, and he had got along well with Stalin when he was in Moscow organizing Lend-Lease. Although suffering from cancer of the stomach, he rose from his sick bed to go. In the event, his talks with Stalin were amiable but accomplished little.

The episode was characteristic of Truman, in his blunt language, his awareness of his limited experience, and his willingness to take advice. It was also characteristic of Washington opinion at the time, wavering uncertainly between firmness toward the Soviet Union and conciliation.

A few people believed that Russia wanted only friendship with America, mostly holdovers from the Roosevelt Administration such as Hopkins, Secretary of Commerce Henry Wallace, and Eleanor Roosevelt, who still had a following. Some others, while harboring no shred of sympathy for Communism, were understanding of Russia's anxieties about security and its desire for a buffer zone of friendly states, and were ready to extend to it the benefit of the doubt. These included Dean Acheson and Henry Stimson, the Secretary for War, an elder statesman who had been Secretary of State under President Hoover. Stimson told the others, when they were discussing relations with Russia, "In my experience, the only way to get a man's trust is to trust him."

Others believed the Soviet Union was implacably hostile, prominent among them James Forrestal.

In February 1946, the US Ambassador to Moscow, Averell Harriman, returned home on leave. He left the Embassy in charge of George F. Kennan, who was, along with Bohlen, one of the group of longtime Soviet affairs specialists in the State Department whose views had been sidelined in the Roosevelt years. Kennan was a thoughtful, introverted intellectual, conservative in his outlook and impatient with the constraints that democracy placed upon foreign policy. He often saw himself as a prophet crying in the wilderness, his views ignored over the years.

The State Department asked for the Embassy's view on the Soviet attitude to the new international financial arrangements. Kennan took the opportunity to send in reply a 5,500-word telegram setting out his vision of the mind-set of the men ruling Russia, their likely behavior, and what the American response should be. His preface showed the seriousness and subtlety of his approach. He said the Treasury's query involved "questions so intricate, so delicate, so strange to our forms of thought, and so important to our analysis of the international environment that I cannot compress the answer into a single message without yielding to a dangerous degree of simplification." In the years since then Kennan has been written about and discussed more than any other American diplomat in history, and the long message from Moscow that first brought him national attention discussed more than any other diplomatic dispatch.

Given the caveat in his preface, it would be foolish to summarize this document, but some of the main points can be stated. The Soviet leaders, because of their background and their ideology, were incorrigibly suspicious of the West, fearful of "capitalist encirclement" and hostile. Their aim was to extend Soviet power both by direct means and by political subversion and they had an international apparatus operating in every country dedicated to accomplishing this. Friendship with the Soviet Union was an illusion. The Soviet leadership was "impervious to the logic of reason but it is highly sensitive to the logic of force." A realistic American policy would be to contain Communism within its boundaries, applying counterforce to Soviet pressure wherever necessary.

The policy was dubbed "containment," although this word was not used in the dispatch, but in an article expounding his view that Kennan wrote the following year for the quarterly *Foreign Affairs*, published by the Council on Foreign Relations. The article appeared anonymously but his identity soon became known.

The telegram arrived just at the time when it would have the most impact, when there was no consensus in Washington and opinion was wavering. As Kennan himself wrote in his memoirs: "Six months earlier this message would have been received in the State Department with raised eyebrows and lips pursed in disapproval. Six months later it probably would have sounded redundant, a sort of preaching to the convinced." During much of his career Kennan was at odds with the culture of Washington. Indeed he often seemed at odds with the twentieth century, looking back fondly to an earlier age when international relations were conducted without the pressures of public opinion and democratically elected legislatures. But at this moment he crystallized the thinking about the Soviet Union in Washington and gave it direction.

James Forrestal, the Secretary of the Navy, was one of those who saw Kennan's long telegram, as the message from Moscow became known. An energetic figure, fiercely competitive everywhere from Wall Street, where he made a small fortune, to the tennis court, he had long argued that the Soviet Union was implacably hostile. The long telegram, coming from an acknowledged expert, seemed to be a masterful exposition of his own view and he circulated it among political circles. He arranged to bring Kennan back from Moscow to be one of the directors of the new National War College.

From then on discussion of American Cold War policy centered on the concept of containment, what it meant and should mean. It was the concept against which policy proposals were measured. Initially it was criticized by some for being too negative, by others as a policy of "wait and see," and by others for its assumptions about the Soviet Union. Later Kennan said his view had been misinterpreted: he had intended containment to be political rather than military. He had made it clear in his original telegram that the Soviet Union was not poised to go to war.

If some officials were finding it difficult to readjust their picture of the Soviet Union as an ally, the public were finding it more so. During the war, the Government and most of the media had promoted a benign image of the Russians as allies in the fight for freedom. For the American and British governments the alliance with Russia was *Realpolitik*; the Soviet Union was "my enemy's enemy." But the public needs sentiments, and an ally had to be a friend. Magazine articles and films showed the bravery, resoluteness, and patriotism of Soviet soldiers and civilians. The Russians, it was said, were people like us, lovers of their country, determined in defense of their homes and families, rambunctious, fun-loving. Stalin was a man we could deal with. They had a different political system but hey, we can all get along.

There was also among liberals a desire to see good in the Soviet Union.

Harry Hopkins, who had acted often as Roosevelt's emissary to Stalin, said, "The Russians undoubtedly like the American people. They like the United States ... They are a tenacious, determined people who think and act just like you and I do." This seems incredibly naïve for a public figure. The Russian people had very little opportunity to express whatever sentiments they may have had toward the United States or any other country.

During the war the public were treated to all the apparatus of officially promoted international goodwill: exchange visits, charity drives for Russian war relief, and symbolic gestures – the Sword of Stalingrad presented by "the people of Stalingrad" to the heavily bombed British city of Coventry. Anyone who drew attention to the totalitarian nature of the Soviet regime, or who cast aspersions on Stalin's good faith, was likely to be accused of bad taste, of abusing an ally, even of mouthing German propaganda. Some of these sentiments among the public lingered after the reason for which they were engendered became inoperative, more so in Britain than America. This was partly because British public opinion was less volatile than American, and partly because British gratitude for Russia's war effort, especially during the period when it was Britain's only fighting ally, was more heartfelt.

Here is the British historian E. P. Thompson recalling the 1945 election campaign in rural Buckinghamshire: "Packed meetings of suddenly undeferential villagers applauded every expression of hope for a Socialist Europe, and every reference to the heroism of the European resistance movements or the feats of the Red Army (which everyone knew had saved what small ration was left of British bacon)."

Here are two items taken almost at random in 1946 from British newspapers hardly sympathetic to Communism. The *Sunday Express*, which supported the Conservative Party, ran an editorial on January 1 pointing out that the Soviet Government had promised its people more clothes, sugar, butter and beer in the coming year and asked why Britain's Labour Government could not do so as well. The *Observer* ran a profile of Stalin, and, while noting the ruthlessness of his actions in Poland and his treatment of political opponents, found a core of virtue: "One might say that in Stalin, ambition and lust for power have not wholly suppressed, but only suspended, his humanely Socialist aspirations." This is typical of the time, censure of the Soviet leader but softened by reference to his "humanely Socialist aspirations." Criticism of Russia in the press was rarely unqualified. Today it is customary to lump Hitler and Stalin together as two great tyrants of the century. At that time this would have been unthinkable in the mainstream media.

Communism was socially acceptable in Britain. There were two Communist MPs, the largest number ever, and a handful of Labour members who supported Communist policies most of the time, and these were treated indulgently. There were organizations to cater to those who were sympathetic to Communism but would not sign up to the party line, friendship societies with this or that eastern European country, and the Unity Theatre, which put on Communist-inspired plays and even musicals which were often reviewed favorably. Communist intellectuals were accepted as commentators in the press. When Penguin Books got a Conservative to write *The Case for Conservatism* and a Labour Party intellectual to write *The Case for Socialism*, it seemed only natural to get one of the two Communist members of Parliament to write *The Case for Communism*.

There was talk in Britain, and in Europe, at this time of a "third force," between untrammeled capitalism American-style and Communism. Attlee said in a New Year broadcast in 1948 that Britain could be a third force between "downright capitalism and tyrannical Communism." He even told the *New York Times* correspondent C. S. Sulzberger in an off-the-record conversation that all Europe could be a third force. He said he envisaged a socialist Britain one day "leading the Socialist nations of Western Europe, which would serve as a bridge between the Communist Soviet Union and the capitalist U.S.A."

Attlee's Government was criticized from the left. Left-wingers were disappointed at not seeing all the revolutionary change that they wanted. The civil service including the Foreign Office was still the same Establishment. The *New Statesman* complained, "British socialism is represented all over the world by men who, in a strictly non-political way, are opposed to every Socialist principle and are hot gospellers for anti-Bolshevik ideologies. And cabinet policy is based on information which these men provide." The Government did not take the radical step of abolishing private schools, to which the middle and upper classes sent their children. These, and in particular a dozen or so top-ranking schools are the principal means by which social and occupational advantage are passed on from one generation to the next. Attlee went to a leading private school, as did several members of his cabinet. The Labour Party leaders were not revolutionaries in the classic sense of the term. They aimed to change society but not to overthrow existing social institutions.

Some in the Labour Party rebelled against Bevin's foreign policy stance in particular. Bevin was getting applause from the Conservatives in Parliament and this seemed wrong. Fifty-six Labour MPs signed a motion calling for more collaboration with socialist countries, which were neither named nor defined, and for a middle course between Communism and capitalism. For many of these, the Soviet Union shared with them the ideology of socialism, although it had a different approach. To take a left-wing stance on domestic affairs, wanting to speed up or extend nationalization, for instance, usually meant being more friendly toward the Soviet Union.

This was confusing ideological with strategic positions. An ideological stance between Communism and US-style capitalism need not imply a strategic stance midway between America and Russia. Yugoslavia was soon to break with the Soviet bloc and find itself on the end of abuse and threats while remaining a Communist country. As the French Socialist Party leader Guy Mollet said, "Communism is not to the left. It is to the east."

Anti-Americanism was not only political. Many in Europe had an unfavorable image of America, seeing it as a brash, materialistic, philistine, aggressive country, a threat to peace and to cultural values. A survey among British people in 1946 showed that older people tended to see in Americans boastfulness, immaturity, materialism, and immorality, while younger people had a more congenial image, citing energy, generosity, enterprise, and efficiency. (In literary circles American literature and theater were widely admired. The left tended to be anti-American politically but pro-American culturally.) Greeks among the Romans was still an image in many British minds: the British Greeks, worldly-wise, sophisticated, cultured, among American Romans, strong, raw, immature, requiring guidance. Even Americans succumbed to it, a phenomenon known to students of psychological power-plays as "colonial cringe." During the war, American academics assigned to the British code-breaking center at Bletchley Park were warned against becoming "slavishly Anglophile."

Culturally, older people in particular saw Americans as representing the lowest common denominator. The guardians of European culture felt themselves to be fighting a defensive war against the invasion of American entertainment with its own low set of values. A key battlefield of cultural warfare was films. Britain was the biggest importer of American movies and the late 1940s were the high point of cinema-going in Britain. The sociologist Michael Young warned the Government against the "perverted values" of American cinema, "its preoccupation with an unreal world of wealth and trivial emotions and its concentration on the stars." A writer in the quarterly film magazine *Sight and Sound* had another view of the popularity of American films:

> In a Europe that is tired and weary, and in many parts unable or unwilling to help itself, this Transatlantic vitality mirrored in films offers some kind of dream-hope. Peace-weary citizens visit the cinema and for a few hours are

> able to forget the taut unhappy face in the queue and assorted ill-tempered officials and sink into a world that is 100 percent living, where people live life and not just endure it.

The Government put a levy on American film imports and used it to subsidize the British film industry to help it compete. The British film-maker Sir Michael Balcon, the head of Ealing Studios, wanted films that projected a positive image of Britain:

> Britain as a leader in social reform, in the defeat of social injustices, and a champion of civil liberties; Britain as a patron and parent of great writing, painting and music; Britain as a questing explorer, adventurer and trader; Britain as the home of great industry and craftsmanship; Britain as a mighty military power standing alone and undaunted against terrifying aggression.

Yet the best-known films he made at Ealing Studios in the next few years were comedies – "Ealing Studio Comedy" became a brand name. What they celebrated was not Britain's greatness, its leadership in social reform and so on, but its quirkiness, its oddness, and this also was how the British people liked to see themselves. In *The Titfield Thunderbolt* a group of villagers decide to run their own railway, in *Kind Hearts and Coronets* a man eighth in line to a dukedom murders whimsically all those ahead of him so that he can inherit.

Many Ealing comedies reflect a mocking attitude to authority. In *Passport to Pimlico*, the inhabitants of that little area of London use an ancient document to declare their independence, tear up their ration cards, and give two fingers (the American equivalent is the middle finger) to the authorities. In *Whiskey Galore*, a group of Scottish islanders gleefully plunder a cargo of whiskey washed up on their shore and outwit the officials who are trying to reclaim it. In *The Lavender Hill Mob* a trio of respectable lower-middle-class Londoners plan the perfect crime. These are the ways that British people rebel. They are not natural revolutionaries.

McDonalds and Starbucks had not yet made their appearance but Coca-Cola, which arrived in Europe with the American Army, was seen as a symbol of the American invasion. When Coca-Cola set up a manufacturing plant near Marseilles, this became a controversial issue. The French Communist Party denounced the project and demanded that the Government halt it. Some claimed that the drink was addictive. A rumor spread that it was intended to put a huge Coca-Cola poster opposite Notre Dame Cathedral. One newspaper demanded, "Are we being Coca-Colanized?" and the term stuck. Winegrowers' organizations claimed that Coca-Cola damaged public health and said French people should continue to drink wine instead. A sugary drink manufactured in Atlanta versus one made from the fruit of the vine going back to Biblical times, hallowed by tradition and with sophisticated variations, was a set of antipodes that seemed to confirm cultural stereotypes. The French Ministry of Finance, responding to public pressure, denied Coca-Cola permission to build the Marseilles plant on the ground that the profits would go back to America and be a drain on the balance of payments. The company said it would keep the profits in France. In 1949 the National Assembly passed a law regulating the manufacture of soft drinks which created new restrictions. Eventually the plant was built.

Also, of course, America was helping Europe, and everybody resents being helped. A British radio comedy show at the time featured an American who, after a comic line, would say, "That's a great joke, kid. Here, have a food parcel." An American visitor hearing this joke was upset by its anti-Americanism.

Meanwhile, the Soviet Union was still projecting to many a benign poster image. It is described in what was hardly a parody by Peter Sellers' Communist shop steward in the film *I'm All Right Jack*. He would like to visit Russia, he says, and adds, looking dreamily into the distance, "All them fields of ripe corn, and ballet in the evening."

Relations between the Soviet Union and the West at that time were like a marriage in which the quarrels gradually come to predominate over more amicable exchanges but the parties are reluctant to consider a divorce.

Some issues were argued out at a series of conferences of four foreign ministers – France being represented along with the Big Three. At the meeting in Paris in May 1946, Britain and America and the Soviet Union clashed over Greece, over Trieste, which was disputed between Communist Yugoslavia and Italy, and over eastern Europe. At the meeting in London Russia asked for bases in the former Italian colony of Libya; Bevin wanted them for Britain. But at the next meeting, in Paris in October, agreement was reached. Libya was given independence and Trieste was to become an international city under UN supervision – it soon reverted to Italy. At the next meeting in London, peace treaties were agreed with the smaller enemy countries. There were few difficulties. Bulgaria was restricted to a naval force of no more than 7,250 tons; the Bulgarian Navy consisted of one ship of 7,250 tons.

The Soviet Union said it should share in the control of the Dardanelles, the straits linking the Black Sea to the Mediterranean, which would have infringed Turkish sovereignty. Truman said this was unacceptable and sent the battleship *Missouri* on a visit to Turkey to underline the point. The demand was dropped.

There was a more serious conflict over Iran. British, American, and Soviet troops had been stationed there during the war to facilitate the passage of supplies to Russia, and it was agreed that they would all leave by March 1946. But Soviet troops remained and then sponsored a Communist rebellion in the province of Azerbaijan, on the Soviet border. The issue was taken to the UN Security Council, the first major issue to come before it. The United States and Britain stood firm and Russia pulled back its troops.

As in the war, faraway places were featuring in headlines in America, and seemed to be important. This was worrying to Americans who had thought that from now on they could concentrate on their domestic affairs. In 1946 only 7 percent of Americans thought foreign relations were a more important issue than domestic matters.

But the couple were not prepared for a divorce. Secretary of State James Byrnes still spoke of "our Russian friends." When newspapers referred to "the Allies" they usually meant America, Britain, and Russia, as they had during the war.

Germany was where the wartime Allies met on the ground. They had agreed at Potsdam that it would be divided into four occupation zones, Soviet, American, British, and French, but governed as one unit. The US State Department was insistent on giving France an occupation zone, although it had not taken part in the Potsdam conference, to help restore French national pride. The occupation commanders met regularly in Berlin and in the early days at least coordinated some activities and entertained one another. But the Russians ran their zone without reference to the Western powers.

The Russians took reparations, as agreed, stripping bare the industry in their zone. They carried away industrial machinery that could have put Germany back on its feet and let it rust in railroad sidings because nobody could use it. Later, they realized that this was mistaken and they let machinery stay in Germany so that it could produce goods that they could appropriate. Reparations were sent home from the American and British zones also, but in 1946, in the face of a lack of cooperation from the Russians, this was halted. The Russians held elections in their zone from which Western observers were banned and maneuvered the Communist Party into power.

Everyone was arguing over Germany. The French objected to American and British plans to revive German industry. They had been invaded three times by Germany and they were worried above all else about a German revival. They wanted Germany lamed; this would be achieved by French annexation of the Saar and a separate regime for the Rhineland, two areas bordering on France, with a permanent military occupation. The Americans did not like Britain exporting its socialism to Germany and nationalizing industries in their zone. The State Department, which determined policy toward Germany, argued with the War Department, which had the task of governing it, and General Clay several times threatened to resign over what he considered a neglect of German interests. He cabled the State Department that he hoped "it will not be forgotten in our political warfare with the USSR that we have here in Germany 70 million human beings to remember."

European countries that had suffered at German hands feared German domination of the continent once again, and something even worse, a German alliance with the Soviet Union. Memories went back to the Treaty of Rapallo, which had shocked Europe in 1921. That was when, as European diplomats met in conference in Genoa, the representatives of the two outcast nations, defeated Germany and newly Bolshevik Russia, slipped away to Rapallo and signed an agreement to cooperate, behind the backs of the others. And then of course there was the closer Soviet–German pact of 1939.

General Clay was worried about German morale. Communism still had some appeal in West Germany, although this diminished as the brutality of the Soviet occupation became apparent, but many Germans did not want to associate Germany with the West, preferring it to adopt a neutral stance. Clay was a Southerner, the great-nephew of Henry Clay and the son of a Georgia senator, and he knew something about the humiliation of defeat and the reactions that it could produce. He was an old friend of James Byrnes, a former North Carolina senator and fellow Southerner. Partly on his initiative, Byrnes visited Germany in September 1946 and made a speech in the opera house in Stuttgart. Clay stage-managed the occasion to ensure that it was a significant event.

Byrnes recalled that after World War One America had retreated into isolationism and went on: "We will not make that mistake again. We intend to continue our interest in the affairs of Europe and the world." As for Germany: "Americans have long since ceased to talk of a 'hard peace' or a 'soft peace' for Germany. Freedom from militarism will give the German people the opportunity, if they will but seize it, to apply their great energies and abilities to the works of peace." Now Germans had something to look forward to. As an American official remarked, "That was the end of Morgenthauism."

As a safeguard against a revived and aggressive Germany, Britain and France signed the Treaty of Dunkirk in March 1947, promising to come to one another's aid if there was ever again a threat from Germany. Even a year later, in a cabinet meeting, Sir Stafford Cripps said they should make up their minds whether Germany or Russia was a greater danger. Bevin said he was trying to steer a middle course, another minister said they should build up Germany as a barrier against Russia, while Dalton insisted that Germany was the greater danger and "greatest of all in combination with Russia."

In France General de Gaulle stepped down from the premiership. He had headed a coalition government, but he was disdainful of the dealings that are a normal part of democratic coalition politics, and he formed his own right-wing movement – he would not call it a party. Before he resigned he took up the idea of Jean Monnet to develop a plan to modernize French industry. The plan was embarked upon and carried on through all the turmoil of the succeeding years. Monnet had been an international financier working in many countries and had served the French Government in two world wars. He never ran for public office but he was one of the most important figures in postwar France and, a lifelong internationalist, he was to be one of the founding fathers of the new European institutions.

The Communist parties in France and Italy were not at that time acting as revolutionary parties. Stalin did not want a Communist revolution in France or Italy because he was sure the Americans would move in to crush it, and he did not want America back in Europe in force. He told the Communist parties in those countries not to try to seize power. Instead they were to participate in government as national parties. The Western powers did not know at the time that they had been instructed not to seize power. In any case, Stalin's message was no guarantee that they would not take advantage of a collapse into chaos. Stalin gave the same advice to the Chinese Communist leaders when they visited Moscow: don't attack the Nationalist Government but make your peace with it and bide your time. They thanked him, went back home and did the opposite and became the rulers of China.

The French Communist Party announced itself as the party of production, working to increase the country's industrial efforts. Party Secretary Maurice Thorez declared: "We are for the revolution tomorrow. Today we want capitalism to work." They presented themselves as patriots, and they were as forceful as anyone in their demands on Germany. Sometimes pursuing this tactic violated their political instincts. Thorez criticized striking miners for "adventurism" when most Communists were sympathetic to them. The issue of French Indochina was painful. When the Government asked for funds to fight the Communist-led rebellion there, the Communists could not vote against this and remain in the Government. In an uneasy compromise, Communist deputies in the National Assembly abstained in the vote while those in the cabinet supported the policy.

The Italian Communist Party was also playing the parliamentary game. As one party official said, "Our symbol now isn't the hammer and sickle but the gavel and sickle." In a move that surprised everyone, the Communist deputies even voted alongside the conservatives for the continuation of the Lateran Pact that gave the Roman Catholic Church a special role in the Italian state. They gained in popularity, particularly in the rural south, by developing local welfare services, taking care not to mention revolution or Lenin. The Communists were as likely to organize a picnic or holidays for children from working-class families as a political demonstration.

Unlike Europe, America did not move leftwards after the war. The Republicans won the congressional elections of November 1946. To many Americans, the wartime expansion of government controls was simply a continuation of the process begun by President Roosevelt with his New Deal. In their election campaign, Republicans pointed to the mass of regulations and campaigned with the slogan "Had Enough?" As beef and pork disappeared from shop windows because farmers refused to sell at regulated prices, people blamed the shortage on the Democratic Administration. "Who made you a vegetarian?" was one slogan.

Candidates flaunted their war records in a way that would have been unthinkable in Britain. Joseph McCarthy, who was to achieve fame in the Senate as an anti-Communist demagogue and give his name to a kind of political witchhunt, said in his campaign literature that, although exempt from military duty, he had volunteered and had flown as tail gunner in the Marine Air Force, while his opponent Robert LaFollette Jr "enjoyed his Senate salary and fat rations." This was a lie, the start of a career based on lying. McCarthy was not a tail gunner but a ground intelligence officer. Richard Nixon was running for Congress. His election literature described him as "a clean forthright young American who fought in defense of his country in the stinking mud and jungles of the Solomon Islands," while the incumbent Jerry Vorhis "stayed safely behind the lines in Washington." This was stretching the truth. Lieutenant Nixon had served in the Solomon Islands, at a naval air station, but there was no call for him to fight in or even visit the stinking mud and jungles. John F. Kennedy's managers in his campaign for a congressional seat ensured that voters knew all about his exploits as a motor torpedo boat commander.

The Republicans made Communism an election issue. The *Republican News*, the official paper of the party, said a section of the Democratic Party was "dedicated to Sovietizing the United States." In working-class areas of Detroit and Chicago, where many voters were of eastern European origin, Republicans accused Roosevelt of "selling out" - the phrase was used often - their countries at Yalta. The Catholic hierarchy reminded its flock of the Catholics of eastern Europe condemned to live under atheistic Communism.

In the rural South threats kept most Afro-Americans away from the polling booths. Some candidates ran as racists. One of the most notorious was Mississippi Senator Theodore Bilbo, who said, "I call upon every red-blooded white man to use any means to keep the Nigger away from the polls. The best way is to have a little talk with him the night before the election." A move to refuse Bilbo a Senate seat because of pronouncements like this failed. He was later found guilty of taking a $100,000 bribe, but died before action could be taken on this.

The elections left the Republicans in control of both Houses of Congress for the first time since 1932. They were in a position now to reverse fourteen years of high government spending and to slash budgets. President Truman would have to battle with a Congress dominated by the opposition party, and anyone who wanted the Government to spend money would have a fight on his hands. Congress blocked many of Truman's welfare proposals and passed the Taft–Hartley bill on labor relations, which reversed some of the pro-union legislation enacted under Roosevelt.

It was a conservative Congress, and, while its members were willing to live peaceably with the Soviet Union, most were instinctively anti-Communist. Conservatives have a visceral hostility to Communism. For these, Nazism was a phenomenon that had suddenly arisen and, once it was clear that it could not be accommodated, had to be fought. But Communism was the eternal enemy. It was seen as an organized threat from below to order, decency, and civilization. Southern congressmen saw moves toward racial integration as Communism. J. Edgar Hoover, the Director of the FBI, described Communism as a disease that, if not checked, would infect American life. Anti-Communism in America in the ensuing years sometimes took forms that violated both civil liberties and common sense, and meant the persecution of liberals and the corruption of many areas of American life. The election of the 1946 Congress made these things possible.

Most Americans were anti-imperialist, by history and sentiment, and so was President Roosevelt. When Roosevelt and Churchill drew up the Atlantic Charter in 1941 setting out their war aims, one of these aims was that people should have the right to govern themselves, "to choose the form of government under which they will live, and to see sovereign rights and self-determination restored to those who have been forcibly deprived of them."

To Roosevelt and to most Americans, it meant just that. But to Churchill it referred only to peoples under enemy occupation, not to colonial empires. Roosevelt pressed Britain to promise India independence after the war. He wanted independence for Malaya and also for French Indochina and thought Hong Kong should be returned to China. In parts of Asia, Americans and British clashed at the political level and sometimes on the ground. Americans in SEAC, the Southeast Asia Command headed by Lord Louis Mountbatten, said the initials actually stood for Save England's Asian Colonies.

Americans had a favorable view of Britain, particularly after the war, and regarded Britain's possession of colonies as a character flaw one could overlook most of the time, like a fond uncle's unfortunate habit of getting tipsy every now and again. The British supported their fellow-imperialists in the Far East. British troops helped the Netherlands retake the Dutch East Indies (now Indonesia) as the Japanese pulled out. When the Japanese surrendered in Indochina a British force went into Saigon to restore order so that the French could come back.

Roosevelt told Lord Halifax in 1945: "France has had Indochina for nearly a hundred years and the people are worse off." During the war men of the OSS – the Office of Strategic Services, the forerunner of the CIA – parachuted into Japanese-occupied Vietnam and worked closely with Ho Chi Minh and his Vietminh guerrillas, and these seemed to share his view. Ho expressed admiration for American institutions. OSS officers noted Ho's popularity and recommended US Government support for him. But strategic thinking in Washington predominated over anti-imperialist sentiments. Ho Chi Minh was a Communist. Nationalism may have been spurring the revolt but the Communists were directing it. Dean Acheson cabled the American mission in Saigon that in the view of the State Department, "the least desirable eventuality would be the establishment of a Communist-dominated Moscow-orientated state in Indochina." The Vietnamese who learned to shoot and took to the jungle may have thought Ho was fighting to get rid of his French overlords. So far as the US State Department was concerned, he was engaging in a worldwide struggle for Communism.

Shortly afterwards the United States formally recognized French sovereignty, while favoring eventual independence. The United States thus found itself supporting a European power in its imperialist war. Later it would replace it.

As 1946, the first full postwar year, came to a close, things in Europe seemed to be moving, slowly but in the right direction. Britain's export earnings were rising and had reached their prewar levels. In France, Belgium, and Holland, industrial production was up to 90 percent of its prewar level. The lawlessness that followed the liberation had faded in France and Italy and their governments were setting about organizing economic recovery. Most of the French railway system was repaired and German industry was beginning to function again.

In two countries occupied by Soviet troops, Hungary and Romania, there was political freedom and coalition governments in which Communists were in a minority. It seemed that the Soviet Union would not prevent the establishment of democracy there. The United Nations General Assembly had held its first meeting, in London.

In Britain it was as thin a Christmas for festive food and drink as it had been in wartime, but people were looking forward to things returning to normal by the following year, when you would be able to go to the shops and buy what you wanted providing you had the money. George Orwell wrote in his weekly column in the magazine *Tribune* on December 20: "I wish everyone an old-fashioned Christmas next year, and in the meanwhile, half a turkey, three tangerines and a bottle of whiskey at not more than double the legal price."

CHAPTER THREE

LIKE A YOUNG MAN PUSHED OUT ON HIS OWN

Twice in the tumultuous decade that was the 1940s, weather changed the world. In 1941 the Russian winter came earlier than expected, halting the German blitzkrieg in the snow and dashing hopes of a quick victory over the Soviet Union and, as it turned out, of any victory at all. In 1947 the cold winter created a desperate situation in Britain and all of western Europe that signalled an end to British imperial power.

The *World Factbook* says the British climate is "temperate, moderated by prevailing Southwest winds over the North Atlantic." And so it is. Britain does not get very hot or very cold. It is not exposed to hurricanes or tornadoes. Apart from the north of Scotland and some hill areas, there is rarely more than two inches of snow. British people do not keep the appurtenances needed in more extreme climates: tire chains, galoshes, storm cellars, home air-conditioning units.

In the first months of 1947, however, the weather was not mild, it was extreme, the coldest winter in Britain since weather records were kept. The record low temperature was accompanied by snow and gales. In the Britain of today such weather would be disruptive and damaging. In the Britain of 1947 it was catastrophic.

The year began with a government white paper issued on January 1, which told British people that if they wanted a brighter future they had to produce more. It said that even though export earnings were up, the country was still buying more abroad than it was selling, and warned that if exports were not increased, "we may never recover the foundation of our national life."

Britain needed to increase production. But the weather brought production almost to a halt. Snow began to fall on the night of Thursday, January 23 and it went on falling. Within two days the whole country was covered in snow. For the next seven weeks, snow fell every day somewhere in Britain. The temperature dropped to freezing and remained there. At midnight on January 28, Big Ben struck twelve and then fell silent, its works frozen solid. The next day the Thames froze at Windsor.

There was a brief respite in mid-February but then more snowfalls came, heavier than ever, and blizzards. For weeks on end a biting east wind blew in from the North Sea. People shivered in threadbare clothes they could not replace because of clothes rationing, and came home to draughty homes with only a small fire or inadequate central heating because coal supplies were cut off.

Rail travel was stopped in many places because snow piled up on the tracks and points were frozen. Commuters could not get to work. There were no snowploughs in London and other towns in southern England and roads were blocked. Violent winds blew the snow into drifts ten and twelve feet deep in areas where people had never seen such things before. The RAF was called out to drop food supplies, and huge four-engine Halifax bombers flew low over the Staffordshire countryside and the Yorkshire dales. Farming was hit hard. A million sheep were lost and 50,000 head of cattle.

The crisis was first of all a coal crisis. Stocks were low. Britain burned 200 million tons of coal a year, and the previous winter reserves had fallen to less than two weeks' supply.

Coal was the key to the Industrial Revolution. The Industrial Revolution began in northwestern Europe where there was coal under the ground which could power machines. In 1947 coal was the principal fuel for power plants, factories, and railroads. In Britain, 93 percent of manufacturing power was coal power, and a coal fire in the grate provided the heating in a lot of homes. This accounted for the grime on the buildings in industrial towns, and the acidic tang in the air in wintertime that scratched the throat, as well as the regular bouts of fog in London, fog that sometimes reduced visibility to a few feet.

The Labour Government had nationalized the coal industry and this took effect on January 1, 1947. The miners' union was left wing and militant, but now union officials sat on the boards running the mines, replacing their bitter enemies, the mine owners. But they took over an industry in trouble. Coal owners had allowed the mines to run down; they had invested only 25 percent of their profits back in the mines, compared to 75 percent in the American coal industry. Productivity in 1947 was below the 1939 figure. The best seams, closest to the surface, were mined out. There was a shortage of manpower; 40 percent of coal miners leaving the armed services did not go back to the mines. The Government wanted to recruit miners among the 50,000 Poles who had served with the Allied armies and now remained in Britain rather than returning to a Communist Poland. It says something of the political atmosphere of the time that the Cabinet were told that the miners did not like the Poles because, so far as they were concerned, if they did not want to return to their Communist homeland they were fascists.

The cold weather froze machinery at the pits. It blocked railway lines so that coal could not be delivered to industry. Ice closed ports in the northwest, so that the ships that normally brought coal to industrial towns could not sail. Coal was not delivered to homes. Some people went into the countryside to chop down trees for firewood.

Attlee addressed the country over the radio. He appealed to people not to use electricity or gas between the hours of nine o'clock in the morning and twelve noon, or between two and four o'clock in the afternoon. "We have come through greater emergencies and much more critical times. We will come through this if we pull together, each doing everything possible to help," he said encouragingly. Four days later it was clear that this appeal was not enough, so the Government made it illegal to use domestic electricity between those times. On Friday, February 7, the Government suspended electricity supplies to industries in London, the Midlands and the northeast. BBC television went off the air and the radio closed down at nine o'clock in the evening. This was more disruption than the Luftwaffe had ever achieved. J. L. Hodson, back from the Middle East, out of the Army and at university, wrote in his diary:

> I lie without lights. My bedroom is rather dark so I cannot read. I cannot listen to the radio. I cannot sit up in bed and do anything since the power is off and I cannot use my electric fire ... I hate the cold. I wish I was back in Egypt. I wish I were anywhere but in this goddamned country where there is nothing but queues and restrictions and forms and shortages and no food.

Factories were shutting down and sending their workers home and soon two million people were out of work. This brought back bitter memories of prewar unemployment, just what the Labour Party had promised would never be repeated. Every area of life was hit. Publishing houses ran out of paper so magazines did not appear, pubs ran out of beer.

Yet the crisis could have been foreseen and at least the worst aspects avoided. Some ministers had warned the previous summer that coal stocks were not enough for the winter and that industry should cut back. Douglas Jay, one of Attlee's economic advisors, wrote a memo back in June saying that at the present rate of usage coal would be short in the winter. The one man who did not foresee the coal shortage, indeed denied that there would be one, was the man in charge of coal supplies, the Minister of Fuel and Power, Emmanuel Shinwell. Shinwell, a Scot, was a sixty-three-year-old former union leader of apparently unquenchable optimism. The previous October he had declared in Parliament, "I want to tell you that there is not going to be a crisis in the coal industry." He pointed to nationalization and said there was now "a new spirit in the pits." He wrote a memo to Attlee, countering anxieties about coal: "You should not allow yourself to be led up the garden path by statistics. You should look at the imponderables," he said. When, after these assurances, Shinwell told the Cabinet that stocks were now so low that they would have to cut supplies to industry, Hugh Dalton exclaimed in his diary, "This is a complete thunderclap, following on the usual rather hopeful tales we have had from this man during the past week."

The privation was worse than anything most had suffered during the war. The journalist Anne Scott-James wrote about the plight of the housewife: "The fuel shortage is the worst thing that ever happened to her. Food is difficult but it can just be managed, and she could always provide enough for the children by going short herself. But to see them looking pinched with cold was a misery, and her own spirits fell to zero after hours spent between a frozen outdoors and a chilly house." John Strachey, the Marxist intellectual turned social democrat, was Minister for Food, and someone coined the phrase "Shiver with Shinwell, starve with Strachey." (Later, Strachey became Minister for War and said merrily when he took office, "Having been Minister for Food when there was no food, I trust I shall be Minister for War when there's no war.")

Spirits were lowered further by a permanent grey sky. The observatory at Kew reported no sunshine between February 2 and 22. Diary entries as the winter went on reflect a mood of depression bordering on despair. Maggie Joy Blunt wrote: "The battle against this long winter, the continual government crises and blunders, the cold, wet delayed spring and everlasting austerity has exhausted us all to the bone. Our nerves are on edge, our anxieties and depressions enormous." Some had a bleaker outlook still. Edie Rutherford wrote: "Husband said once again a good thing we can't see ahead, adding that if we could have seen in 1940 what victory meant, many would have committed suicide rather than go on with it."

Americans looked across the Atlantic and saw a worrying picture. The *New York Times* warned in an editorial: "The world could lose the balancing wheel of British moderation, the weight of Britain on the economic scale." *Newsweek* asked in a cover headline, "Will There Always Be an England?"

The cold weather affected the whole of Europe. In prewar years Britain and Germany had both exported coal to the rest of Europe. The German mines were still not back to pre-war production levels and Britain had none to export. In France and Italy strikes were spreading and there was a widespread mood of discontent. People on an industrial workers' salary could barely feed a family and many never ate meat. Every country suffered. Norway's daily food ration was down to 2,200 calories. The shortage impeded recovery. Germany could not send steel to France for ball bearings for industry because it was not producing the coal to make the steel. Scandinavia did not send timber for badly needed housing to other countries because, not receiving imports of coal, it was burning timber for fuel.

America was shipping coal to Europe, 40 million tons a year. This was expensive since coal makes a bulky cargo. Coal that cost five dollars at the pithead in West Virginia cost $20 by the time it reached its European destination. But it was needed. French Prime Minister Léon Blum, facing the threat of increasing disorder, asked Truman for more coal urgently. On this, he said, hangs "our economic reconstruction or our political destruction."

Britain began the year with a serious balance of payments deficit. The freeze-up practically halted exports and made the deficit much worse. Cabinet meetings were now dominated by discussion about how to cut government spending.

Overseas commitments were an obvious place to look for cuts, yet this was difficult to contemplate because it was overseas commitments that made Britain a world power. Hugh Dalton, the Chancellor, wanted cuts in the armed forces. Bevin and Defence Secretary A. V. Alexander resisted. Dalton wrote to Attlee on January 20: "We cannot afford either the money or the men for which the Ministry of Defence asks ... We are drifting in a state of semi-animation towards the rapids." Dalton, a professional economist and a socialist, was known for the vehemence of his attacks on the Conservatives in debate. Now he was having to battle with his own colleagues, and particularly with Bevin.

Greece was one questionable commitment. Britain had 9,000 troops in that country and was subsidizing the Greek Army. The situation there was deteriorating. The war was being fought in dozens of small battles and the guerrillas were winning more of them and expanding the area they controlled. The morale of the soldiers sent into the mountains after them was low. Attlee had been in favor of pulling back from the Mediterranean anyway and he was losing faith in the Greek cause. He wrote a memo pointing to the lack of progress, and said: "Politically, the present Greek Government is not one about which the Labour Government can feel any enthusiasm. We have already spent far more than we can afford on Greece, and in my view the time has come when we must refuse to enter further commitments." Dalton added his voice: "I regard the Greeks as a very poor investment for the British tax payer."

Bevin, still a firm believer in British power in the world, pointed out that Soviet troops remained in Bulgaria on Greece's northern border, and said Britain should not pull out until they could be sure that the Communists would not take over. The British ambassador in Athens, Clive Norton, warned that an announcement that aid was to be withdrawn would have a devastating effect on the Greek Government and on the morale of the armed forces.

The issue was finally thrashed out at a meeting of a cabinet committee on February 18. Bevin arrived breathing heavily from the strain of climbing two flights of stairs because the elevator was not working. Dalton said they must cut the aid to Greece. Bevin again pointed to the danger of a Communist victory and the Greek dependence on outside help. Well then, Dalton said, if Greece needed outside help it could turn to America. Britain would not just pull out but invite the Americans to take over. After all, the US Secretary of State had said America stood by the Greek Government. And while they were at it, they would remind America that the Turkish armed forces needed some help in facing up to Soviet pressure over the Dardanelles, and Britain, traditionally the dominant outside power in the area, could not at this point supply it. "That seems fair," Bevin said. Dalton told his Treasury officials to draft a note to the British Embassy in Washington, to be given to the Secretary of State. Then they both went back to grappling with the pressing day-to-day problems.

The message to Washington reminded the American Government that the Secretary of State had said Greece and Turkey must not fall to Communism. It explained that the Greek economy was on the point of collapse, and that without help there would be "widespread starvation and consequent political instability." Britain had given Greece £40 million in financial aid since the liberation and had troops stationed there. But now, it went on, "in the light of the grave problems of overseas finance which we ourselves have to face, His Majesty's Government have decided that they cannot undertake further commitments." Aid would stop on March 31. It was accompanied by another note saying Turkey also needed help and Britain could not provide it.

Although it was Truman who had appointed James Byrnes Secretary of State, the two men did not work well together. A longtime North Carolina senator and chairman of the Democratic Party, Byrnes thought he should have been chosen as Roosevelt's vice-president, which would have meant that he would now be in the White House. He did not defer to Truman but acted independently. This was not a satisfactory state of affairs, and in January 1947 he resigned. Truman appointed General George C. Marshall to replace him. It was an appointment that was universally popular.

Truman wrote on his appointment calendar, "He is the great one of his age." Marshall had been Army Chief of Staff throughout World War Two. He had not been in the headlines as much as Eisenhower or MacArthur, but he was admired in Washington for his judgment and his organizing skills. Once out of the Army he was immediately recalled to duty to take on a hopeless mission to mediate between China's Nationalist Government and the Communists. He was experienced at negotiating with Congress and had the respect of both Houses. He was a non-political Secretary of State who assumed that the office was above party politics. He never voted in elections because he thought that as a military officer it would not be right for him to express opinions on party issues.

He was a commanding figure of authority and rectitude. Working constantly with Roosevelt, he never had the casual, jocular relationship with him that others had, and insisted on addressing him as "Mr President" rather than "Franklin." He himself was always addressed as "General Marshall." He lacked the ego that is a driving force behind most public figures. Charles Kindleberger, who worked for him in the State Department, said of him, using the kind of language that others have used: "He was a great man, a man who was Olympian in his moral quality. He was a man who, when he made a decision, everybody knew nothing small or calculating went into the decision." Marshall once told his senior staff at the State Department: "I shall expect of you complete frankness, particularly about myself. I have no feelings except those that I reserve for Mrs Marshall."

Marshall liked an orderly administrative structure and created a tighter organization at the State Department. He set up a Policy Planning Staff, to take a broad view of foreign policy issues beyond the day-to-day concerns that crowd in. "You can't operate and plan at the same time. They're two different mind-sets," he explained. He asked George Kennan to become its head when he had finished his term at the War College, later in the year. Kennan had a creative mind, more suited to broad conceptual thinking than day-to-day administration, as his career had shown.

Marshall also was thinking about Greece. The US ambassador there, Lincoln McVeagh, like the British ambassador, was sending warnings that the Government was in danger from the Communist insurgency and said aid was needed. McVeagh was not a career diplomat. Originally a classics scholar, he had been in his Athens post since 1933 apart from the war years, and was equally at home in classical and modern Greek. His word was listened to in

Washington. He warned that Communist success in Greece would be a setback for American interests. Marshall told the State Department to prepare a plan for aid to Greece, and by February they had one worked out.

On Friday February 21, Marshall left the State Department early in the afternoon to attend the bicentennial celebrations of Princeton University and receive an honorary degree. Then the British Embassy telephoned to say it had two urgent notes to deliver. The Under-Secretary, Dean Acheson was in charge at the Department in Marshall's absence. Protocol dictated that the ambassador should not deliver messages to anyone but the Secretary of State, so as these were urgent Acheson asked the Embassy's first secretary to deliver them rather than wait until Marshall's return on Monday. The first secretary, H. M. Sichell drove over to the Department through the rain and presented the notes to Loy (short for Loyola) Henderson, the head of the Near East section. Henderson showed the notes to John D. Hickerson of the European section. They decided that the matter was urgent, and took them at once to Acheson. Recalling this episode in later years, Acheson wrote, "They were shockers."

It was not being asked to provide aid to Greece that was shocking. The State Department was already preparing a plan for aid. It was the fact that Britain was pulling out and proposing to hand over responsibility. After all, the US Joint Chiefs of Staff had advised the previous year: "The defeat or disintegration of the British Empire would eliminate from Eurasia the last bulwark of resistance between the US and Soviet expansion ... Our present position as a world power is of necessity closely interwoven with that of Britain."

This was a momentous change. For two centuries Britain had been the dominant power in the eastern Mediterranean. Now it seemed to be surrendering that role in two key countries. It is often said that Americans lack a historical sense that Europeans have, but on this occasion it was the Americans who saw the historical significance of that moment. To British ministers, battling from day to day to keep the country's head above water, this seemed to be just a temporary retrenchment in one area. None of them appeared to see any larger implications in the decision. The American view was put in grandiloquent terms by Joseph M. Jones, who was in the State Department at the time: "Reading the messages, Hickerson realized, as had Henderson before him, that Great Britain had within the hour handed the job of world leadership, with all its burdens and all its glory, to the United States."

Acheson decided that this was going to be a busy weekend. He told Henderson and Hickerson to get members of their staffs together and assign them tasks with a view to drawing up reports on Greece's situation, what resources were needed, what resources were available, and the significance of Greece and Turkey to western Europe. He also told them to talk with military and naval chiefs. Then he telephoned Marshall and told him that this was the most important decision he had had to take since the war. Henderson called a meeting, which he asked George Kennan to chair, and it went on until nearly midnight.

Greece was in danger: that much was clear. As for Turkey, Soviet pressure for a share in the administration of the straits leading to the Black Sea had been lifted when America showed its concern and sent the battleship *Missouri*, but it would probably be resumed if there was an indication that America was no longer interested.

The officials worked all weekend, with working groups producing reports, sending them to Acheson and revising and combining them. On Sunday evening Henderson took the draft reports to Acheson's house in Georgetown. Henderson said he was not clear on one point. Were these papers, he asked, about deciding on a policy, or about carrying out a policy that had already been decided upon? Acheson said, "We're going to do it, Loy. Work on that basis."

Then, he recalled in his memoirs, "We drank one or several martinis to the confusion of our enemies."

Dean Acheson, the Under-Secretary of State, later to become Secretary of State, gave his memoir of his time in the State Department the title *Present at the Creation*, and he was indeed present at the creation of the world of the half-century or so after World War Two. The title contains an element of modesty, not a characteristic usually associated with Acheson, for he was not merely a spectator at the creation but one of the creators.

Acheson was born in Connecticut into the Anglophile East Coast Establishment. His father was a Canadian-born Episcopalian bishop and the family always celebrated the King's birthday. He attended Groton, the elite private school, and then Yale. He joined the prestigious Washington law firm of Connington and Burling and rose rapidly in the legal profession. He served for a while in Roosevelt's Administration as Under-Secretary of the Treasury, and, back in private life in 1940 and 1941, he argued for aid to Britain in its war effort. When war came he went into the Government again as Assistant Secretary of State for Economic Affairs, then became Under-Secretary.

He was a tall elegant figure with the bristling moustache of a British cavalry officer. He had confidence in his own intellectual powers, usually justified, a gentlemanly code of conduct, and a brisk practical approach to the problems of the world. He coined the acronym "bomfog" for "brotherhood of man, fatherhood of God" talk, indicating his dismissive attitude to rhetoric floating high above the realities of power and to those who indulged in it. He had a biting wit that could be cruel, and was often accused of arrogance. Minnesota congressman Walter Judd, who often dealt with him as a member of the Foreign Affairs Committee, said once, "Acheson was always dignified but there was a certain condescension. It was like he was sorry for us hayseeds." Despite this, Acheson could see qualities in people whose background and intellect were very different from his own. He established a close relationship with Ernest Bevin, and developed admiration and warm affection for President Truman.

He and Truman had one characteristic in common: strong personal integrity. Two episodes illustrate this. Truman owed his political career to Tom Pendergast, a Kansas City alderman and power in local politics, and a friend. Pendergast subsequently served a jail sentence for corruption and was shorn of all his political power. When he died Truman had been vice-president for a week; he commandeered an Air Force plane and flew down to Kansas City for the funeral, knowing that this would expose him to criticism. When Alger Hiss, a senior State Department official, was accused of espionage for the Soviet Union, Acheson, a personal friend, said, "My friendship is neither given nor withdrawn lightly. I will not turn my back on Alger Hiss," a statement which drew fire from right-wingers. The elegant phraseology could not be Truman's but he would have shared the sentiment.

On the Monday morning after that busy weekend, February 24, the British ambassador, Lord Inverchapel, called on Marshall and formally presented the notes again and they discussed them. Then Acheson went off to a long-planned lunch with an old friend, the journalist Louis Fisher, at the Metropolitan Club. Fisher found him distracted and uninterested in his food. Unburdening himself, and speaking off the record, Acheson gave a picture of the new world he saw coming into being. "There are only two powers left," he said. "The British are finished. They are through. And the trouble is that this hits us too soon, before we are ready for it."

Over the next few months he struggled to adjust to this new world, in which American was thrust into the foreground. He did not at first realize, as he said later, how fundamental was the change that was taking place. As he recalled later in an interview: "It didn't really strike home to us that the British Empire was gone, the great power of France was gone … I still looked at the map and saw that red on the thing, and, by God, that was the British Empire."

This was far more than a transfer of the burden of supporting two countries' armed forces. British power in the eastern Mediterranean did not rest on the presence of British arms or even British money, although the Royal Navy was a familiar sight in those waters. Britain was the power those countries looked up to, the place the elite or would-be elite sent their children to be educated, the model for parliamentary democracy for those who were interested in democracy, or for a modern monarchy for those who supported a monarch. Britain was the country that, in the case of Greece, would take the crucial decision of what government should be supported. Whether they liked it or not, whether they knew it or not, the British were withdrawing more than aid for the armed forces.

The British scholar and writer C. M. Woodhouse, long a close observer of Greek affairs, observed the Greek reaction waspishly:

> Alert Athenian politicians, applying such simple and conclusive tests as that of the size, quantity and opulence of the motor cars rolling through the streets, were already convinced that Britain's day was ending and America's was dawning. Those who had devoted years to proving that they were practically natives of Claridge's now turned their energies into proving that they were practically indistinguishable from Southern Democrat senators.

The CIA's Miles Copeland saw the difficulties from the agency's point of view: "The OSS had left an impressive array of secret intelligence assets in Europe, but there was little to replace those of the British in Greece, Turkey and other countries which comprised the new vacuum."

Shown the British notes, Truman had no doubt about what to do. America had to step in. New legislation would be needed and the next step was to persuade Congress to pass it. He needed time. Marshall sent a telegram to Bevin saying that it would take more than six weeks to get the necessary governmental machinery going to get aid to Greece, and asked him to postpone the deadline. Bevin agreed to do so.

Truman summoned leaders of the Senate and House of Representatives to the White House for a meeting with himself, Marshall and Acheson which took place three days later. Marshall addressed the legislators first. He was not a powerful speaker and he focused not on the spread of Communism but on the immediate plight of Greece and on Britain's poverty. Congress members asked, "Aren't we just bailing out Britain again?" and "What is this going to cost?" Acheson decided that Marshall had not hit the right note and that things were not going well. He whispered to him, "Is this a private fight or can anyone join in?" Marshall told the others that Acheson wanted to say something.

Acheson gave them the big picture. He jolted them with an alarming account of the advance of Communism: the Soviet Union tightening its grip in eastern Europe, pressure on Iran and Turkey, Communists in the governments in France and Italy, and now the civil war in Greece. He said Britain was so weakened financially that there were now only two great powers in the world. Not since Rome and Carthage, he said, had there been such a polarization of power, and it was between democracy and dictatorship. Aiding Greece and Turkey would be defending America and defending freedom in the world. He added that there might be other such crises and ended with a warning: "We are at the point of decision. We cannot enter upon the first step of this policy without the assurance and determination to carry it through."

After he had finished speaking there was a silence lasting several seconds. Then Senator Arthur H. Vandenberg, the majority leader in the Senate, turned to Truman and said, "Mr President, if you say that to Congress and the country, I will support you and I believe most members will do the same." Truman promised that he would do just that.

Truman addressed a special session of both Houses of Congress on March 12. His speech had been written by teams of people in the State Department and the White House, but its tone was characteristically Truman's: simple and hard-hitting. He began by describing the plight of Greece, ravaged by war and now by the attacks of what he called Communist-led terrorists. He said Greece was urgently in need of help and Britain could no longer supply it. He went on: "The United States must supply this assistance. There is no other country to which democratic Greece can turn."

Given the attention paid to Greece and Turkey in recent weeks the request for help was not unexpected. But then Truman broadened the issue. "At the present moment in world history nearly every nation must choose between alternative ways of life," he said. These were representative government with civil liberty on the one hand and dictatorship on the other. "I believe," he went on, "that it must be the policy of the United States to support free peoples who are resisting attempted subjugation by armed minorities or by outside pressures." This was the key sentence and the wording reflects Truman's attitude. When the draft had been shown to him he made two changes. The draft proclaimed that "it should be the policy of the United States." He changed it to "*must* be." And the draft spoke of "free peoples in the Middle East". He cut out the reference to the Middle East, removing any limitations.

He asked Congress to appropriate $400 million for aid to Greece and Turkey and to authorize the dispatch of American civilian and military personnel. He concluded: "Great responsibilities have been placed upon us by the swift movement of events. I am confident that the Congress will face these responsibilities squarely."

The speech had gone through several drafts and many people in the State Department and the White House had had an input. While it was in draft form, several people expressed doubts about it. George Elsey, a White House aide who worked on an early draft, complained about its sweeping nature: "There has been no overt action in the immediate past by the Soviet Union which served as an adequate pretext for 'all-out' speech. There have been other instances - Iran for example - where the occasion more adequately justified such a speech, and there will be other occasions - I fear - in the future." He also worried that aid to Greece and Turkey would mean "getting into European politics."

A draft was shown to George Kennan. He also objected to the apparently unlimited commitment, and he thought it might provoke the Soviet Union to aggressive action. But these views were overruled. A final draft was shown to Marshall when he was in Paris, on his way to the four-power foreign ministers' conference in Moscow. He also thought it hit the anti-Communism button too hard and commented, "It's overstating the case a bit." The White House replied that it felt that Congress would only respond to a strong anti-Communist message and this was what Truman wanted. Certainly the speech must have come as a surprise to the Soviet Government. It was a response to action by Britain, not by Russia.

Newspapers immediately dubbed the theme of the speech the "Truman Doctrine," by implication comparing it in importance to the Monroe Doctrine promulgated in 1823, which told European powers to stay out of the Americas. Most approved of it. The *New York Times* declared in an editorial: "The epoch of isolationism has ended. We are now in the epoch of American responsibility." In another section of the paper, James Reston reported the attitudes of members of Congress to finding themselves in this new epoch. "Most of them," he said,

> are still so bewildered by the implications of the wider issues of accepting or rejecting world leadership that they spent most of today bewailing the fact that they had to face them at all ... Like a young man suddenly pushed out on his own and forced to assume responsibilities he had always thought would be comparatively easy, the legislators are finding the realities of world leadership more troublesome than the theory.

In Britain Truman's speech was officially welcomed, but the Foreign Office assistant permanent under-secretary, Gladwyn Jebb, wrote in a memo that it was "a badly thought-out and impetuous gesture" which would make Soviet–American cooperation in the United Nations impossible.

The BBC broadcast a weekly *American Commentary*, and that week it was done by the American journalist Joseph Harsch. He devoted it to Truman's speech. Hugh Dalton heard it at his home at 11 Downing Street. "History rose up this week and dealt American thinking a staggering blow," Harsch said.

> America has been asked by its political leaders to take the longest, broadest and most meaningful step in the nation's history out beyond the established frontiers of its influence. If one of the purposes which motivated the decision in Whitehall to end British financial aid to Greece on 31 March was to make America think about its world role, then that purpose has been achieved …
>
> London might just as well have dropped an atomic bomb on Washington; the impact would have been no more startling … The President is dealing with a Congress which took office fully expecting that it could, and confidently predicting that it would, cut expenses, cut taxes, cut the army, cut foreign commitments and cut foreign responsibilities. Now he asks them to assume responsibility beyond the wildest dreams of any pre-1947 American internationalist or interventionist.

Dalton listened to this and reflected in his memoirs: "My little push for a small economy in Whitehall had released world forces far more powerful than I had ever guessed."

Truman's speech was criticized from the right and the left. It was attacked by old-time isolationists who thought America should not spend money abroad and should have as little to do with foreigners as possible. The left criticized its anti-Communist interventionism. Henry Wallace, the Secretary for Commerce, had left the cabinet as his views became increasingly incompatible with Truman's. He went to Britain at the invitation of the left-wing magazine *New Statesman* and addressed a meeting, telling the British people not to be carried along with Truman's anti-Communist crusade. (He judged his audiences well. In America he warned Americans against being used to shore up the British Empire; there was no such message when he spoke in Britain.) He went on to Stockholm with the same message. His criticism of Truman abroad infuriated many Americans and Vandenberg called him an "itinerant saboteur."

One objection, in Congress and in the press, was that the aid to Greece and Turkey would bypass the United Nations. Americans at that time had high hopes for the UN, as did many others. Working through it would be their way of intervening in world affairs while sharing responsibility. They expected the organization to be placed at the center of global policies. Vandenberg decided that the Administration had blundered in ignoring the United Nations. He drew up with Texas Senator Tom Connally an amendment to the aid bill which said the aid was being given only because the United Nations could not provide it, and that it was in full conformity with the UN charter. This was accepted. Vandenberg usually had to put his own stamp on a measure before he would approve it.

Senator Vandenberg did not initiate the vast changes in America's direction in the world that were now beginning, but he facilitated them. He was a key figure in getting Senate approval for aid to Greece and Turkey, as both the Republican leader of the Senate and Chairman of the Foreign Relations Committee, just as he was to be a key figure in getting approval for the Marshall Plan. Vandenberg was the editor and publisher of a newspaper in Grand Rapids, Michigan, a grave, jowly figure usually smoking a cigar, who could be self-important and vain but was deeply sincere. Before the war he was the leader of the isolationists in the Senate. Although he was sympathetic to Britain in its war against Nazi Germany, he fought against any measures that might associate America with the war effort. But in January 1945 he announced that he had undergone a conversion. He said that in the contemporary world America could no longer isolate itself but had a role to play. He became a member of the US delegation to the conference that set up the United Nations.

Vandenberg was in the chair when hearings on aid to Greece and Turkey began before the Senate Foreign Relations Committee, a necessary prelude to the Senate debating the bill. With Marshall away in Moscow, Dean Acheson represented the State Department. Senators were worried about how far Truman was committing America. He had talked about free peoples resisting subjugation. Did this mean that America was pledged to intervene in the same way in every situation in which a nation's freedom was endangered? Acheson assured them that no worldwide ideological crusade was contemplated. He said every situation would he considered differently. He gave the example of Hungary; the United States had protested when the Soviet Union engineered a Communist takeover but recognized that there was not much more that it could do.

Inevitably, the question arose: if Greece, then why not China, the most populous country in the world, where the Government was also fighting a civil war with the Communists? Acheson could only point to the aid that the United States had already given to China, and say that the situations were quite different. Then one after another, officials gave evidence and answered questions, including Henderson, and McVeagh from Athens, as well as military men.

One exchange showed Acheson's hardening attitude to the Soviet Union. Senator Alexander Smith asked whether the aid program "will press Russia to really sit down with us and settle some of these differences". "Senator," Acheson replied,

> I think it is a mistake to believe that you can at any time sit down with the Russians and solve questions. I do not think that is the way our problems are going to be worked out with the Russians. I think they will have to be worked out over a long period of time and by always indicating to the Russians that we are quite aware of what our own interests are and that we are quite firm about them and quite prepared to take necessary action. Then I think solutions will become possible.

When some senators objected to supporting a reactionary monarchy, Vandenberg said they were not supporting the monarchy but helping the Greek people. McVeagh told them, "The choice is between an imperfect democracy and totalitarianism." This was a choice America was to face often in the future, between a reactionary or repressive government and a Communist one.

An exchange between Dalton and Acheson at this time shows British ministers' failure to understand the situation in Washington, dealing on the ministerial level and ignoring the sensibilities of Congress. Dalton suggested that, as they had been asked to delay the withdrawal of troops, and this cost money, could not the Greeks pay Britain the cost of keeping the troops there out of the dollar aid they were receiving from America? Acheson was appalled by this suggestion. He had been sweating it out with congressional committees and facing charges that America would be "pulling Britain's chestnuts out of the fire." If it turned out that some of the money that was to be given to Greece ended up in British pockets, congressmen would go ballistic. He told Lord Inverchapel that pursuing this would be folly.

The bill was passed, by 67 votes to 23 in the Senate and 287 to 108 in the Lower House. However, the size of the majorities concealed doubts about spending and about further involvement in Europe. Senator Francis Case of South Dakota told Truman, "The policy was regarded as an accomplished fact. You had spoken to the world. At least 75 members, I would judge, would have voted against final passage, myself included, had it not been that we thought it would be like pulling the rug out from under you or Secretary Marshall."

Most of the bill concerned Greece. Aid to Turkey was military aid, a small program to strengthen the Turkish Army. Plans to aid Greece were already under way. Reports from Athens persuaded the Administration that it should not give aid unless it could intervene to ensure that the aid was used well and that it would have a lasting effect.

On March 3, two weeks after the British notes, the Greek Government addressed a request for help to the United States. It asked, not only for financial and military aid, but also for American personnel to ensure that aid was used effectively, and "to help to restore a healthy condition in the domestic economy and public administration, and to train the young people of Greece to assume their responsibilities in a reconstructed economy." This request from a sovereign government may seem excessively humble, even humiliating, but it met American needs. This is not surprising since it was drafted by the State Department.

In the months after the passage of the bill American aid started to arrive in Greece and Americans along with it. The aid included food and clothing but also military material. The United States sent the basic equipment a modern army needs, such as radio sets and jeeps. It also sent aircraft to bomb guerrilla bands in their mountain hideouts, and then napalm to drop on them.

The Americans who went with the aid brought advice and strong pressure to accept the advice. Dwight Griswold, a former governor of Nebraska who had been an economic official in the American occupation zone in Germany, went to Greece as head of the US economic mission, and General James Van Fleet went as head of the military mission. Both sat on Greece's Supreme Defense Council. The Greeks found they had to accept Griswold's advice on economic matters and Van Fleet's on military matters. The Americans insisted that the Athens Government close down a Communist newspaper, curb Communist-led trade unions and purge the civil service of suspected Communists.

After a government reshuffle, Prime Minister Konstantinos Tsaldaris, the leader of the People's Party, decided to form a government only of People's Party members. Griswold decided this would be too narrowly based to be stable and told him it was unacceptable. Tsaldaris objected to the language so Griswold changed it to "inadvisable." Loy Henderson came from Washington to explain just how inadvisable it was. He told Tsaldaris and Themistocles Soufolis, the leader of the Liberal Party, that failure to cooperate could mean the end of American aid. They formed a coalition government with Sofoulis as premier and Tsaldaris as foreign minister. Henderson did not have everything his own way, however. He would have preferred Tsaldaris as premier as the stronger man.

A week after Truman's speech, there was another trumpet blast summoning Americans to the ramparts. This came from one of the leading intellectuals of the day, James Burnham, with a new book, *The Struggle for the World.* Burnham's earlier book *The Managerial Revolution*, published in 1940, was regarded as one of the major works of the century, a book about economics that ranged far beyond economics. Its thesis, in crude summation, was that a new class was emerging that comprised not the ostensible owners of industry but its managers, a class with its own interests and values which would manipulate and control society, and that this had its counterpart in politics. Any new book by Burnham was going to be taken seriously, and the editors of *Life* magazine brought this one before a mass readership by spreading his message across twenty-one pages. It said in an editorial that this was an important book.

The Managerial Revolution had insights but at this distance some of Burnham's judgments seem like simple power worship. Hitler was seen as a successful representative of the new managerial class, Stalin a less successful one, but both had created ideologies that inspired people, as the liberal democracies did not. Burnham was a former Trotskyite, and he retained from Marxism a belief in historical determinism. The managerial class was inevitably going to come to power and was going to advance its interests because that was what a class does. He said we cannot hope to change the course of history but only to "alter by a degree or two the rate or direction of its advance."

He gave hostages to fortune by making forecasts. He said Germany would probably win the war. He said that if Roosevelt ran for president again in 1940 and won (which he did), that would probably be the last free election in America, and if he ran again and won in 1944 (which he did), that would certainly be the last free election. He said that America would take over the British Empire, and that three centers of power would emerge from the war based in America, Germany and Japan.

The fact that the world in 1947 bore no resemblance to the world he had foreseen does not seem to have prevented his new book, *The Struggle for the World,* being taken seriously. According to his thesis World War Three had begun already. The war was between the West and Communism, and it was to be all consuming. He demonized Communists as people who "sacrifice family, friends and moral beliefs for one passion, the will to power." Communists and all their works must be fought everywhere abroad and the Communist Party should be banned at home. The only alternative to a Communist empire was an American empire, although it would not be called that and America need not rule other countries directly.

Burnham recognized that Americans were not ready for this task: "No people, pushed by forces they cannot control, ever entered on the paths of world power with less taste for the journey, with more nostalgic backward glances." Nonetheless, "The United States has made the irreversible jump into world affairs. It is committed everywhere, on every continent, in every major field of social action, and it can never again withdraw." Thousands of *Life* magazine's readers wrote in response. Some praised it; a naval chaplain offered a prayer of thanks. Most were against, describing it as a counsel of despair. *Life*'s editors said two-thirds were opposed.

Nevertheless, the book, coming at the time it did, reinforced Truman's picture of a world divided into two camps, implacably hostile to one another. The picture was a false one. Most countries were neither Communist nor democratic. Nor were individual Communists the demons Burnham conjured up, consumed by a passion to advance their cause beyond any other moral considerations.

The essence of drama is conflict and drama is what gets people's attention. It may have been true, as Truman said, that the situation had to be presented in these terms to shock Congress and the country into supporting the necessary measures. He was to summon up this picture of conflict again and again to get support. But a spirit of conflict once whipped up cannot be easily shut down. Others were all too ready to accept the image of a titanic struggle between good and evil with a threatened America in the thick of it. Such a conflict rests easy on the brain. It requires little reflection and leaves little room for self-questioning. The need to fight overrides other considerations. Truman was adding strength to a current that was already under way.

He himself was carried along by it. Nine days after his speech to Congress, he signed a bill for a loyalty program designed to attack subversives in Government. A Communist spy ring had recently been uncovered in Canada. The bill required the setting up of loyalty programs in every government department and the investigation of new employees. Truman disapproved of the bill but he was under pressure from Congress. Government employees ranging from ambassadors to janitors in federal buildings came under the programme. It developed in many areas of American life into an obsession with domestic Communism, as if this were a major threat to the nation.

The House of Representatives UnAmerican Affairs Committee was holding hearings designed to flush out Communists as enemies of American life. Sixteen members of the Anti-Fascist Refugee Committee were arrested for refusing to turn over their books. Later in the year the committee moved to Hollywood to investigate Communist infiltration into the film industry. This gave an opportunity for a number of film stars to perform on the witness stand. Adolph Menjou said Reds should go to Russia. Gary Cooper said he had never read Karl Marx but from what he had heard he did not like it. Ten scriptwriters and directors refused to answer questions about their political activities and were sent to prison for contempt of Congress. The President of the Screen Actors' Guild spoke some cautionary words about the investigation. "I abhor the Communist philosophy but I hope we are never prompted by fear of Communism into compromising many of our democratic principles," Ronald Reagan said.

The Chairman of the committee was J. Parnell Thomas, who advanced his career by accusing people indiscriminately of disloyalty or of being "unAmerican." He turned out to exemplify Samuel Johnson's dictum that patriotism is the last refuge of the scoundrel. He was convicted of filching government money by inventing expenses, and sent to the federal prison in Danbury, Connecticut, where he found himself alongside some of the men he had sent there.

All over Europe there was more damaging cold weather and then a thaw that brought flooding with disastrous effects on crops and cattle. In France there was no electricity one day, no transport another, and gross inequalities. From Paris Sam White reported in the London *Evening Standard*: "Most Parisians are on a diet almost entirely of vegetables, and there are very little of those. In the shops there is no meat, no offal, no fish, no potatoes, no cauliflower – except at black market prices, well out of reach of the low salaried or wage-earning Parisians. For the average tourist or wealthy Frenchman, however, menus in smart restaurants differ little from pre-war luxury."

The workers were angry and the Communists could not go on for much longer containing their anger. They were riding two horses, representing themselves as the party of the workers while also being a party of government. Labor unions were growing restive about accepting Communist leadership which tried to dampen down their militancy. The breaking point came with a strike at the government-owned Renault car plant in Paris. The Government condemned the strike. The Communist Party backed it, and the Prime Minister, Paul Reynaud, dismissed the Communists from his Government.

Two days later the World Bank, which had been established in December 1945, approved a new loan to France. This was its first loan. Its President was John McCloy, the former Wall Street banker recently returned from his position as US High Commissioner in Germany. Soon the French Government began removing Communists from senior positions in the civil service and the police. The withdrawal of Communists from the coalition Government began a period of political instability, with cabinet posts shifting and governments falling every few months, and bad-tempered debates in the National Assembly which at times spilled over into uproar.

However, even in those first post war years of disorder and deprivation, creative spirits emerged, and France still produced trends that swept the world. A group of intellectuals among whom Jean-Paul Sartre was the most prominent introduced the term "existentialist" into popular culture. Existentialism was a movement in philosophy that dated back to the previous century, but Sartre created his own version, portraying a world without values in which Man must create his own purpose and his own terms for living. More than Sartre's work on philosophy, his novels and plays were read and performed around the world, as were those by his philosophical comrade Albert Camus. Notable among these were Camus' novel *The Outsider* and his play *Antigone*, Sartre's novels *Nausea* and *Roads to Liberty* and his plays *In Camera* and *The Flies*. Both men were to be awarded the Nobel Prize for Literature.

Existentialism also gave its name to a youthful lifestyle, cool, anti-romantic, detached, its characteristic fashion plain black. It spread out around the Western world from two clubs on Paris's Left Bank, the Tabou and the Club St Germain-des-Prés. People who never read a line of philosophy talked about things being existentialist – a song, a mood, a person. A ditty in a London revue went:

From Mayfair to Montmartre
It's Jean-Paul Sartre,
And every little tartre
Quotes Jean-Paul Sartre.

Paris, in the person of the little-known dress designer Christian Dior, also produced the New Look that swept the Western world. Dior threw away the minimal, functional fashions that had ruled in the years of shortages and, as if pretending that the hoped-for new world of leisure and plenty had already arrived, brought out a style of dress that emphasized elegance and femininity with an hour-glass shape and mid-calf-length skirts. Being longer and more voluminous than current women's wear, the New Look demanded yards of material. It became a global talking-point. The fashion press went wild. *Vogue* said: "There are moments when fashion changes fundamentally. This is one of the moments." *Harper's Bazaar* reported: "Paris swells with femininity. The big story is a curving, opulent day silhouette that is the most elegant fashion for decades."

(The New Look and social inequality produced one of the decade's more memorable sequences of news photographs. One of the glossy fashion magazines decided to photograph the new style against the backdrop of a street in one of Paris's poorer areas where some homes did not even have running water. Women taking water from a pump were angered to see a model flaunting this finery. They shouted abuse, then started tearing the chic clothes off her. The model screamed for help but the photographer allowed professionalism to win over gallantry and continued to photograph the scene. The sequence was printed in *Life* magazine.)

Because its lower hemline and its styling required more material, the New Look – the term was coined by the press – was widely denounced as a wasteful frivolity. Clothes rationing in Britain allowed women one new dress every year and two yards of knitting wool. In America also clothes were restricted: dresses must be limited to two inches of hem and seventy-two inches around.

Bessie Braddock, a leading Labour Party figure, denounced the New Look as "a ridiculous whim of idle people." The President of the Board of Trade, Sir Stafford Cripps, asked the Guild of Creative Designers to keep skirt-lengths short. *Picture Post*, the socially conscious weekly magazine, said of these fashions: "They are launched upon a world that has not the material to copy them, and whose women have neither the money to buy, the leisure to enjoy, nor in some designs, even the strength to support these masses of elaborate materials." In America also the look was censured for extravagance, and some women staged demonstrations against it saying they wanted to go on showing their legs.

However, Dior had caught a mood. Women were fed up with the years of grimness and getting by with necessities. In America and Europe women wanted the new fashion and wherever they could they flocked to buy it. In Britain, where clothes were rationed and women could not buy a new dress just because the fashion had changed, they sewed a band of another material above the hem to make it longer, so that skirts with a horizontal stripe also seemed a new fashion.

Some other items in the newspapers in America at this time were to resonate in the future.

General Eisenhower scotched once and for all reports that he might run for the Presidency. "I would not accept the nomination even in the remote circumstance that it were tendered to me," he told a New Hampshire newspaper publisher, six years before he entered the White House. No one who knew him, looking back, thought that Eisenhower was insincere. He just changed his mind.

The 1947 World Series was televised. One hundred and seventy thousand American families now had television sets, and many others began to have a vision of watching a baseball game in their own living rooms. The broadcasting network offered advertising spots but advertisers were cautious.

In New Mexico and Arizona, several people saw mysterious objects in the sky and said they looked like saucers. Soon people all over America were seeing flying saucers, and even south of the border there were sightings of *plativolos*. The term flying saucer was more descriptive and more widely used than the official term, unidentified flying objects, or UFOs.

Bernard Baruch, adviser to presidents over five decades, unveiled a bust of himself in the legislature in his home state of South Carolina. In his address he used a phrase suggested to him by Herbert Swope, the former editor of the *New York World* and a close advisor. "Let us not be deceived," he said. "We are in the midst of a cold war." Walter Lippmann liked this term to describe a fierce conflict between nations in which there is no shooting. He used it as the title of a book that year, *The Cold War*, and the term came into the language.

CHAPTER FOUR

A SPEECH AT HARVARD

While Dean Acheson was telling a Senate committee that one could not sit down with the Russians and solve problems, General Marshall was in Moscow trying to do just that. The four-power foreign ministers' conference, one of a regular series that had begun in 1945, lasted six weeks, from March 10 to April 24, 1947. Marshall went there still hopeful that they could reach agreement on Germany, and so did Bevin. It was a frustrating experience for both men.

By this time the CFMs, as the Council of Foreign Ministers meetings were known, had developed set ways of working whichever capital they were in. The ministers sat at a table covered by green baize. Each minister had three assistants at the table and several sitting behind. The seating was, clockwise, Americans, French, British, Russians, and the chairmanship rotated each day in the same order. Since there were three official languages, English, Russian, and French, every speech had to be translated twice paragraph by paragraph. This made for a slow and tedious procedure, and the people around the table spent a lot of time doodling on the pads of paper in front of them while the translators droned on. Sometimes they used the time for whispered conversations in which they prepared replies to what was being said. Meetings were usually held in the late afternoon. In the mornings the teams would read the overnight cables from their capitals and prepare.

The slow procession of speeches, the dogged hostility of the Soviet Union to Western approaches, sometimes grated on people's nerves. Charles E. Bohlen recalled an episode at one CFM meeting. As he told it, the Soviet minister Vyacheslav Molotov was obstructive throughout the afternoon and then they adjourned for dinner. "After liberally imbibing at dinner, Bevin, who had been increasingly irritated and frustrated, returned to the conference in a belligerent mood. When Molotov attacked Britain for past sins in international affairs, Bevin rose to his feet, his hands knotted into fists, and started towards Molotov saying, 'I've had enough of this, I 'ave,' and for one glorious moment it looked as if the Foreign Minister of Great Britain and the Foreign Minister of the Soviet Union were about to come to blows." Security men moved in and the incident was smoothed over.

At another CFM, in Paris, one session was enlivened by the arrival of Bevin and Acheson, arm in arm, singing the socialist anthem "The Red Flag" to show Anglo-American solidarity. Actually, Bevin was singing it and Acheson was going dum-de-dum. Bevin had suggested this to Acheson, whom by now he was addressing as "me lad." Acheson protested that he did not know the song so Bevin told him the tune was the same as "Maryland, My Maryland" and he could just hum along.

At the meeting in Moscow Germany was the only item on the agenda. All the parties had agreed the previous year to set permanent limits on German industrial development and therefore on the German standard of living. The Americans and British had by now merged their two zones into one, with the Ruritanian-sounding name Bizonia. They argued with the French, who still wanted to annex the Saar, establish international control of the Ruhr, where most of Germany's heavy industry was located, and impose stricter curbs on German steel production. However, the others sometimes found it difficult to deal with the French Foreign Minister, Georges Bidault, because, as Edward Mason, a member of the American delegation, observed, "he was drunk a good deal of the time and obviously an emotionally disturbed man."*

The most important differences were between the West and the Russians. Marshall protested at the tight control that Russia was imposing in its zone, restricting freedoms and installing Communists in positions of power. He raised a proposal that had been mooted before: a four-power agreement to keep Germany disarmed for twenty-five or fifty years, with strict controls. The Russians tied this to their idea of a centralized Germany and hedged it around with conditions. American officials got the impression that the Russians did not want such a treaty because the United States would play a part in enforcing it and this would mean an American presence in Europe for many years to come. The Russians, they felt, wanted America out of Europe.

The Russians were keen to take their $10 billion in reparations, some of it from the Western zones. Given the devastation that Russia had suffered at the hands of the German invaders, the British and Americans were sympathetic to the demand for reparations, and had agreed to it at Potsdam. But Marshall and Bevin pointed out that since America and Britain were subsidizing their occupation zones, this would mean that they would be financing reparations going to the Soviet Union.

Near the end of the conference Stalin, who had played no part in it,

* Bidault, a liberal Catholic and former resistance leader, remained Foreign Minister and was Prime Minister for a time, and helped steer France towards integration into the Western alliance. He was a man of stature but his drinking made him seem a buffoon sometimes. French journalists in particular were familiar with this problem but did not report it.

received Marshall, along with the American ambassador, Walter Bedell Smith, in the Kremlin. Bohlen was there to translate. He had last seen the dictator fifteen months earlier, in December 1945, and noted that he had aged since then, looking greyer and more careworn. Marshall had some complaints. He said ships given to the Soviet Union under Lend–Lease had not been returned and communications had not been answered. Stalin apologized and said these things were due to wartime disruptions. Stalin had a complaint of his own. Two years earlier, the then American ambassador had asked what credits Russia needed. Stalin had sent a note asking for $6 billion, and had received no reply. Marshall did not know about the note and said it must have been lost. One can presume that Stalin was skeptical of this reply, but bizarrely it was true. Byrnes, who was Secretary of State at the time, said later, "I had placed it in the Forgotten file because I felt sure that Fred Vinson would not press it." Vinson was then Secretary of the Treasury.

Stalin made light of the disagreements at the conference, saying they were mere skirmishes, and that differences could probably be sorted out later. Marshall said he was worried about conditions in Europe. Stalin put his hand on his shoulder in a friendly fashion and said, "Don't worry. We'll take care of that." Marshall and Bevin came away from the conference convinced that there was no hope now of reaching an agreement with the Soviet Union on governing Germany.

More and more, Marshall was becoming preoccupied with the collapsing economies of the western Europe. If the survival of Greece and Turkey as independent nations was important for the United States, the survival of western European countries as going concerns was much more so. He was getting daily reports of the worsening situation. Bidault in Moscow told him that de Gaulle and his new party were gaining strength and, with the Communists also strong, there was a danger of civil war. In Paris the novelist and adventurer André Malraux, a de Gaulle follower, was giving correspondents blood-curdling accounts of preparations being made for guerrilla warfare in the event of a Communist coup. The consensus among the American delegation was that Stalin wanted to let things drift and see Europe slide into hunger and desperation. In such a situation, Russia would have more leverage and the Communist parties in the stricken countries might come to power.

Immediately after Marshall returned he gave a broadcast report to the nation on the conference and swung the subject around to Europe. He said that although they had discussed Germany in Moscow, this topic involved all Europe. German coal mines, railways, and other facilities must be revived to help Europe, he said, and time was of the essence: "The recovery of Europe has been far slower than had been expected. Disintegrating forces are becoming evident. The patient is sinking while the doctors deliberate. New issues arise daily. Whatever action is taken to meet these pressing problems must be taken without delay."

He had called George Kennan from Moscow to tell him he had to leave his post at the National War College and set up the Policy Planning Staff right away. When he got back to Washington he told him its first task would be to produce an analysis of the problems of European reconstruction and recommendations for action, and he wanted it within two weeks. Providentially, when Kennan accepted the post, he had decided that he was weak on economics and he brought in some people from the economic side of the State Department, among them Paul Nitze, who would succeed him as Director of the Planning Staff, Walt Rostow, and Charles Kindleberger.

It was clear that western Europe's problem was deep seated. Traditionally, it had imported much of its food and raw materials from eastern Europe, from the Far East, and from America, and paid for this by exporting industrial goods. Now it was not manufacturing enough to pay for the food and raw materials it needed, and without the raw materials its industry was handicapped further. To take just one example, France and Italy had plant for making ball bearings, vital for industry, but they were idle because those countries did not have the foreign currency to buy chrome steel which was stacked up unused in Sweden. Europe's own food production was down, and everything was made worse by the weather.

Dean Acheson also felt that Europe needed America's help. Truman asked him to take on a chore. He had agreed to give a speech early the following month in Cleveland, Mississippi. But there was a fierce political row going on in the Democratic Party in Mississippi, and if he went down there he would be drawn into it. He asked Acheson to speak in his place.

Acheson was due to resign soon to go back to private law practice. He had wanted to quit earlier but had agreed to stay on for the first six months of Marshall's tenure of office to ease the transition. He wanted to get things moving on help for Europe before he left. He decided to use the occasion to raise the issue of Europe's plight and America's stake in its survival. He told Truman and Truman approved. "I'm going to throw up a ball and it's going to have to come down somewhere," he said.

The speech was to the annual meeting of the Delta Council, an organization of businessmen and farmers in the Mississippi Delta, one of the more prosperous areas of the deep South. This was a social occasion as well as an educational one for the members of the council. Many sat in a college gymnasium to hear Acheson speak, but there was no room for all and hundreds of others, many of them families with children, sat outside at picnic tables under the trees, and heard his talk relayed through loudspeakers. Acheson was in his shirtsleeves, for it was a warm day, and he spoke from notes rather than from a script. But, despite the air of informality it was a serious occasion. He was pointing to a new direction for American policy. "You who live and work in this rich agricultural region," he began,

> whose daily lives are concerned with the growth and marketing of cotton and corn and other agricultural products, must derive a certain satisfaction from the fact that the greatest affairs of state never get far from the soil. When Secretary of State Marshall returned from the recent Council of Foreign Ministers meeting in Moscow, he didn't talk to us about ideologies and armies. He talked about food and fuel, and their relation to industrial production.

Acheson then set out what he called some basic facts of life. Most countries in Europe or Asia had suffered severe destruction or dislocation as a result of the war; two of the great workshops of the world, Germany and Japan, had hardly begun the process of reconstruction; and in Europe "acts of God" in the form of severe and unusual weather conditions had slowed recovery.

He appealed to Americans' self-interest, presenting this situation as a threat to US prosperity as well as to democracy abroad. "Our exports of goods and services to the rest of the world during the current year, 1947, are estimated to total 16 billion dollars, an all-time peace-time high," he said. "This represents one month's work for each man, woman and child in the United States, one month's output from every farm, factory and mine." Imports from abroad, he said, would be about half this amount. America must help countries in need to get back on their feet, so that they could export more and buy American goods. He recalled the blizzards in Europe of the previous winter and said: "Something more than a blizzard has caused Europe's current difficulties. But last winter's blizzard did show up the extremely narrow margins of human and national subsistence which prevail in the world today, margins so narrow that a blizzard can threaten populations with starvation and nations with bankruptcy and loss of independence."

The State Department quietly drew the attention of favored journalists to Acheson's speech. James Reston of the *New York Times* went to see Acheson and asked him, "Is this a new policy or is it just a bit of private kite-flying?"

Acheson said, "You know this town better than I do. Foreign policy is made in the White House."

So at the next Presidential press conference Reston asked whether Acheson's Cleveland speech represented government policy. "Yes. Next question," Truman replied.

Acheson had begun his speech by talking about America's self-interest, saying America needed European markets for its exports. This was confirmed a few days later in an internal report by an inter-departmental group studying Europe's plight. "The situation must be faced immediately," it said. "If it is not remedied Europe will in early 1948 suffer increasingly severe economic, political and social disintegration, the impact of which on the U.S. will be a falling-off of exports and a piling up of surpluses leading to a depression."

Reston and several other well-informed journalists suggested in their columns that the Administration was considering a new large-scale aid program. The UN Economic and Social Council established the Economic Commission for Europe, the ECE, designed to assist cooperation in recovery, and the US Government welcomed this. Another idea was also gaining ground: that America should push those fractious European countries toward unity. An appeal to Europeans to unite signed by eighty-one prominent Americans appeared in the *New York Times* and other newspapers.

With Acheson's ball bouncing around Washington, members of Congress were becoming anxious. Were they going to be asked to give away more money? Vandenberg went to Truman and demanded to know whether the Government was planning to spend a lot of dollars on European aid. He said that if it were it would have to consult Congress from the start. "I want you to understand that from now on I'm not going to help you with crash landings unless I can be there for the take-off," he told the President.

Acheson lunched with some Democratic senators, and these also said they wanted to be forewarned about future plans. They said they had been caught on the hop by the Greek–Turkish bill and if there was to be another request for aid they wanted time to consider it. Brian McMahon of Connecticut warned that if they were presented with a *fait accompli* he would vote against it. "Where is this going to end?" one senator asked. As it was, the United States was sending $350 million in emergency relief to Italy, Greece, Hungary, Poland, Austria, and China. This had been authorized the previous September, and it was to fill the gap that would be left when UNRRA was wound up on June 30.

A major input into Kennan's planning staff and a spur to action came from Will Clayton, the Under-Secretary of State for Economic Affairs. Clayton is less well known than some of the other Administration figures of the time, although there is a Will Clayton Parkway in Houston, where he had his business headquarters, but he did more than any other person to formulate the Marshall Plan and to carry it through, more even than Marshall himself. His ideas went into it, he drove it forward, and he was at the center of all the negotiations to bring it to fruition, both in Europe and in Washington.

Clayton came from a poor family in a small town in Mississippi, left school at thirteen, and rose to create what became the world's largest firm of cotton brokers. He was called to Washington to take up a high-level (and unpaid) post in Roosevelt's wartime Administration and in 1944 he became Assistant Secretary of State. A lanky, energetic, six-foot-three Southerner, who usually walked several miles a day, he was, unusually among wealthy businessmen, a Democrat and a Roosevelt supporter. He was sensitive to Europe's troubles. He was in London when Truman cancelled Lend–Lease and, realizing immediately the impact this would have, went straight to the American Embassy and telephoned the White House to try to get the decision reversed. He had argued for the British loan the previous December, and helped organize the aid to Greece.

Clayton believed with evangelical fervor in free trade and monetary stability. At this time he was spending a lot of time in Geneva at meetings to set up the eighteen-nation trade organization behind GATT, the General Agreement on Tariffs and Trade, intended to promote free trade. He was also learning at first hand about conditions in Europe. At one point he flew back to his ranch in Arizona for a break after suffering a foot infection. On the plane he wrote a long memo setting out his view of the changing world situation and what the United States should do about it. He said the aid to Greece and Turkey was only a stopgap measure. America should give aid, but this should be a broad program to help Europe's economic recovery rather than a series of piecemeal programs. The aid should not be given unconditionally, he added. The Europeans would be required to stabilize their currencies and open up their borders to trade among themselves to ensure that American aid was not wasted.

After sending this memo to Marshall and Acheson he went back to Geneva for the completion of the GATT negotiations, and then visited several European countries. He found the situation even more alarming than before, and he came back and wrote another memo for Marshall and Acheson, this one describing a situation of political and economic crisis.

He argued that the normal division of labor in a modern society had broken down. French acreage under cultivation was down 25 percent and the farmers were feeding the grain to cattle rather than selling it to the cities because they could not buy enough with the deteriorating currency. "Millions of people in the cities are slowly starving ... More consumer goods and restored confidence in the local currency are absolutely essential if the peasant is again to supply food in normal quantities to the cities," he wrote. He said again that America must give aid and this time he was more specific. Europe should be given six or seven billion dollars a year in goods for three years. This should be based on a European plan. He asked the President to go to the American public. "It will be necessary for the President and the Secretary of State to make a strong spiritual appeal to the American people to draw in their own belts just a little in order to save Europe from starvation and chaos (*not* from the Russians) and at the same time preserve for ourselves and our children the glorious heritage of free America."

Clayton was a passionate advocate. He followed up this memo with meetings first with Marshall and Acheson, and then with George Kennan and members of his Policy Planning Staff. He impressed them with graphic pictures of a peasant who would not produce any more than his family could consume because even if he sold his produce he could not buy buttons or thread; a button maker who could not buy food, and could not make buttons because inflation was prompting his supplier to hoard the raw materials. Beyond this he saw the prospect of chaos, disorder, and bloodshed. He regarded this as part of a profound change in the world, with long-term implications. As he wrote in his memo: "The reins of world leadership are slipping from Britain's competent but now very weak hands. These reins will be picked up either by the United States or Russia."

Kennan's staff drew on this in producing their paper for Marshall. It took three weeks rather than the two that Marshall had specified, even though they worked at fever pitch. This was almost literally true in Kennan's case; he started weeping from the strain at one meeting and had to go out for a walk to recover his composure. Starting from scratch they could only produce broad outlines of policy recommendations, but these reflected several ideas that were current around Washington. They said it was up to the Europeans themselves to draw up a program for their recovery, not America. The role of the United States would be to help in drafting such a program and then to support it by financial and other means. This was the point that impressed Marshall.

Every June, at universities and colleges all over America, honorary degrees are given out, distinguished people are eulogized, speeches are made by those so honored, all part of the institution of commencement, marking graduation from college and the start of a new stage in life for the graduates. In 1947, Harvard conferred honorary degrees on T. S. Eliot, Robert Oppenheimer, General Omar Bradley, who had commanded American troops in Europe during the war, Hodding Carter, a Mississippi newspaper editor, the naval architect William Gibbs, and General Marshall.

Just a few days before the event, Marshall decided that he would use it to set out the idea of a program to help Europe. He asked Charles Bohlen, whom he had recently appointed State Department counselor, to write a speech for him, and he gave him Clayton's memos and the Policy Planning Staff's report. Acheson advised him against using this occasion to air his plans because commencement addresses rarely get much press coverage. However, Marshall was anxious about adverse reaction, particularly in the Midwest, and he did not want the spotlight. He wanted to introduce the idea to the American public gradually.

The European public was a different matter, however. Since the initiative was to come from Europe, Acheson thought Europeans should be alerted to what was expected of them. Three days before Marshall's Harvard speech, Acheson had lunch with three British correspondents, Leonard Miall of the BBC, Malcolm Muggeridge of the *Daily Telegraph*, and Rene McColl of the *Daily Express*, at their invitation, at the United Nations Club. He took along the State Department's press officer, Lincoln White.

The lunch began badly. Acheson greatly liked a dry martini. Once, at a lunch at which he was the guest speaker, not having been offered a pre-lunch cocktail, he told his hosts, "No martini, no speech." Before going off to meet the British correspondents he said to White: "If those Limeys offer me sherry, I'm going to puke." Malcolm Muggeridge, who had a patrician manner and a voice as dry as the driest martini, did just that, perhaps assuming from Acheson's sophistication that he came up to his own idea of civilized behavior. He said, "Now, we won't have this horrible habit of having strong liquor before a meal. We shall have some good wine with lunch, or shall we just have some sherry before lunch?" Acheson demurred and got his martini.

Over lunch they talked about the Cleveland speech, and Acheson told them something of his thinking: that Europe needed American help, that the help should be in the form of a long-term program rather than aid packages to meet particular emergencies, and that the Europeans should organize this. He said nothing about the speech Marshall was to give at Harvard three days later.*

At Harvard on June 5, the morning was given over to ceremonial and the

* There are several versions of these events which differ in detail. This account is based on Leonard Miall's, given in an oral interview which is in the Truman Library and which he says he checked with Muggeridge and McColl, and also on Acheson's version in his memoirs.

giving of degrees. Some of those who attended wore scarlet gowns, some top hats and morning coats, some military uniforms. Marshall, a trim, erect figure with pink cheeks and silvery hair, wore a plain grey suit, white shirt and blue tie. Harvard President James P. Conant introduced him as "an American to whom freedom owes an enduring debt of gratitude, a soldier and statesman whose ability and character brook only one comparison in the history of this nation." The audience took this, no doubt correctly, to be a reference to George Washington, and rose and applauded as Marshall accepted the scroll.

Marshall did not make his historic speech at the main commencement ceremony when he received his degree, but after lunch, to the alumni association gathered on the lawn. Despite his commanding air Marshall was not a powerful public speaker. He had a soft voice and would read from a prepared script. His audience listened to what he said attentively but no one was immediately carried away by his message. Some of those seated on chairs at the back could not even hear him.

He began: "I need not tell you gentlemen that the world situation is serious. That must be apparent to all intelligent people." He described the collapse of the European economy, using Clayton's formulations and even many of his words. The division of labor was breaking down, he said. "The farmer or the peasant cannot find the goods for sale which he desires to purchase. So the sale of his farm produce for money which he cannot use seems to him an unprofitable transaction ... People in the cities are short of food and fuel. So the governments are forced to use their foreign money and credits to procure these necessities abroad."

He declared that Europe needed help and that America should do whatever it could to restore the normal functioning of the world economy. "Our policy," Marshall added, "is directed, not against any country or doctrine but against hunger, poverty, desperation and chaos." However, "Its purpose should be the revival of a working economy in the world so as to permit the emergence of political and social conditions in which free institutions can exist." Any help by the United States should be a cure and not a palliative. He went on to the new and essential point in this proposal for aid: "It would be neither fitting nor efficacious for this Government to undertake to draw up unilaterally a program designed to place Europe on its feet economically. That is the business of the Europeans. The initiative must come from Europe ... The program should be a joint one, agreed to by a number of European nations."

Acheson was right about one thing. The speech did not get a lot of attention. In the *New York Times* it was given a single column on the front page; the lead story was Truman's latest protest to Russia about its behavior in Hungary.

The BBC was still broadcasting its weekly *American Commentary*. That week none of the American journalists on its panel was available so Miall was asked to do the commentary. It was to be on June 5. During a regular call at the British Embassy, the press officer, Philip Jordan, asked him whether he had seen the State Department's advance press release of Marshall's speech. An advance copy of a Secretary of State's speech is routine; the State Department press office gave no indication that this one was of special importance. Jordan said he might find it interesting. Miall read it and realized that this was what Acheson had been talking about at that lunch. His broadcast talk was on the same day as Marshall's address, and he devoted it entirely to the speech and its implications.

He explained Marshall's views on aid, and in his closing sentences he made it clear that it was now up to the European countries to act: "Already there was talk of a special session of Congress this autumn if the countries of Europe have by that time been able to seize the initiative. The ball has now returned to them and in the next weeks and months Washington will watch eagerly to see the reaction across the Atlantic ... On Capitol Hill, they are anxious to get away and to have the whole summer and autumn to prepare for next year's presidential election campaign. Whether in spite of this they will reassemble in the autumn depends on the European response to General Marshall's very direct overture today."

Ernest Bevin happened to hear Miall's talk on his radio at home that evening and he was galvanized by these words. At the Foreign Office the next morning he asked immediately for a copy of Marshall's speech. The reaction was: "What speech?" The Washington Embassy had not cabled it. All the Foreign Office could find about the Harvard speech was a short news story in *The Times* headed "Mr. Marshall's Hint." This was not simply because, as has been said, the British Embassy staff in Washington did not see its significance. They had, earlier, sent a cable based on Acheson's Mississippi speech and other information saying that the Administration was considering a large-scale European aid program, and they presumably thought this covered the subject.

The permanent under-secretary, Sir William Strang, suggested to Bevin that they ask the State Department precisely what Marshall meant. Bevin said, "Bill, we know what he said. If you ask questions you'll get answers you don't want." Marshall had said the initiative must come from Europe. So Bevin took the initiative. He telephoned Georges Bidault and three days later he went over to Paris to meet him. The two men announced that they were taking up Marshall's offer.

What was envisaged was an aid program different from any that had ever been seen before. It was to be given not to one country but to a continent, Europe. However, Europe as a political entity, able to send messages to a foreign government and propose schemes for aid, did not exist. It would have to be brought into being.

When Marshall heard from Bevin and Bidault, he called in Kennan and Bohlen, as his two leading Soviet experts, and asked them whether they thought Russia would join the plan. He said he knew he would be asked this at his next press conference. They both said they thought the Russians would not open up their economy and their industry sufficiently to cooperate with the others. Nonetheless, the Soviet Union was included in the offer, as was made clear to journalists. When Marshall was asked what he meant by Europe, he explained that he meant "the continent west of Asia." He did not say so but he knew it would be much more difficult, if not impossible, to sell an aid package to Congress if the Soviet Union were included. However, he did not want to take the responsibility for dividing Europe.

Bevin and Bidault also were worried about Soviet participation. They thought Russia might cause friction and make agreement difficult. Nevertheless, on June 18 they issued an invitation to the Soviet Union, as the other major European power, to join them in Paris to discuss a response to Marshall's offer. The Soviet Union accepted the invitation and the meeting was arranged for the following Friday, June 27. Will Clayton flew over to be on hand. He went to London first, to meet with the British leaders.

Bevin said later that he had seized on Marshall's speech "like a drowning man grabbing hold of a lifebelt." That summer every British minister felt a bit like a drowning man. It was a bad time for Britain and a terrible time for the Government.

The end of the record cold winter was accompanied by a thaw. Melting snow and rainstorms caused disastrous flooding, and 700,000 acres of farmland were lost to floodwaters. In eastern and southern England, roads were turned into rivers and the Army turned out to rescue villagers in boats. They also delivered food but would deliver milk only if a family could show a baby at the window. In parts of London the Thames overflowed into the streets, and small boys earned tips by shopping for neighbors in zinc baths converted into boats. Even after the floodwaters subsided the weather continued to punish.

Summer was accompanied by a drought which reduced crops all over Europe.

Inflation in America meant that Britain had to pay more for what it bought there. The outflow of money went on and the balance of payments continued to get worse. Dalton wrote in his diary that watching the country's reserves drain away was like "watching a child bleed to death and being unable to stop it."

Times became harder still for the British public. The Government cut food imports by £66 million. It halted the importation of dried eggs from America only to restore it after public protests. Rations of meat, fat, and sugar were reduced further. The extraction rate of flour from wheat was increased to 85 percent so the grey loaf became even greyer. Bevin complained in cabinet that this bread made him break wind. The bread ration was reduced to nine ounces a week, and eleven for manual workers. The average calorie intake was lower than at any time during the war. Overseas, British troops were withdrawn from Egypt into the Suez Canal Zone, which saved a certain amount of foreign reserves, but some troops remained in Greece while American aid arrived, despite the February decision to pull out.

Attlee announced that India would be given independence by June 1948 at the latest. Independence for India had always been the policy of the Labour Party and this move was long planned. Nevertheless, coming at this time, the announcement was seen abroad as imperial retreat. Bevin was anxious to contradict this view, at home as well as abroad. In the House of Commons he said, "His Majesty's Government does not accept the view that we have ceased to be a great power ... We regard ourselves as one of the powers most vital to the peace of the world and we still have our historic part to play."

In America the ambassador, Lord Inverchapel, deplored press reports depicting a ruined Britain with its empire crumbling, and offered a piece of advice he attributed curiously to Leon Trotsky. "It is a great mistake to draw conclusions about the strength of a country from the temporary condition of its technical apparatus," he said. The US Administration still regarded Britain as a world power and indeed counted on it to play this role. A Policy Planning Staff document the next month, reporting Britain's plight, stated:

> If Britain does not receive some aid, she would have no choice but to dismantle extensively her defense and imperial commitments. This would mean that serious vacuums would be created in other areas which could be most embarrassing to us and cause us many headaches. Some of these vacuums are ones we might have to fill. This could cost far more than a completion of aid to Britain at this time.

British cabinet papers during these months abound with phrases that denote desperation, such as "crisis," "emergency," and "a way to escape from the present position." They provide a picture familiar to anyone who has struggled with inadequate finances, looking constantly for new areas in which to save, robbing Peter to pay Paul and then borrowing from Paul to pay back Peter. Dalton told the cabinet that the American loan would be used up by the end of November and they would then have only Canadian credits and their final reserves of gold and dollars. "These reserves must only be thrown in in order to make sure of victory in our battle of the gap. They must not be dribbled away in order to postpone defeat for a few months," he wrote in a memo.

Ministers were suffering from the strain of coping with this as well as from the weather. Bevin had had a heart attack the previous summer. He was overweight, drank a lot, smoked incessantly, and never exercised. He once introduced his doctor to the King saying, "He uses my behind like a darts board." Dalton had boils brought on by stress. Herbert Morrison, the Deputy Prime Minister, was in hospital with peritonitis. Several had colds. The Education Secretary, Ellen Wilkinson, died of a heart attack following an overdose of barbiturates. They saw their plans for a better future ebbing away. The cabinet secretary found Dalton, who kept going now on benzedrine and sleeping pills, stamping around his office saying, "It's not fair that dollars should be spent on Strachey's food, Shinwell's coal and Bevin's Huns. Why can't life be better?" In a diary entry of this time Dalton describes lying awake at night adding and subtracting figures: "I saw spectres of mass unemployment, mass starvation, mass imprecations. Sleeping pills could stop this mental arithmetic, but when I woke the next morning there was no new hope."

The British economy was like a boat being swept along by a fast-flowing river toward the rapids. The rapids were the convertibility of sterling, which was due to come into effect on July 15 under the terms of the 1946 US loan. The Government feared the consequences. When July 15 came they were even worse than it had expected. Banks and other financial institutions around the world sold their pounds sterling for dollars or another currency. The country lost $106 million in the first week and by mid-August it was losing $183 million a week. A third of the American loan was wiped out.

The Government asked the United States to release it from its promise to allow convertibility. Sir Wilfred Eady, a Treasury official, went to Washington to explain the need. Treasury Secretary Snyder at first refused, threatening to freeze the remaining $400 million and brand Britain publicly a defaulter. But the Administration relented, and on August 20 it announced that it had agreed to the suspension of convertibility "on an emergency and temporary basis." It was not restored for ten years.

Support for Britain went hand in hand with doubts about the British Government's political orientation. Robert Lovett, the Under-Secretary of State, said that the British Government had shown recklessness in dealing with the July monetary crisis, and that it was determined to establish "a pattern of life based on the Labour Party philosophy." A lot of Americans were troubled by the British Government's socialism. Commerce Secretary Averell Harriman was concerned that the Government might soon be in the hands of the left wing of the Labour Party. Lewis Strauss, a member of the US Atomic Energy Commission, even told the commission's Chairman, David Lilienthal, that he was concerned about Britain producing an atomic bomb because it might move so far to the left that it would give information about it to the Russians.

The British public were aware of the desperate situation. Just as, in wartime, every newspaper reader becomes a military strategist, following in maps the lines of advance and retreat, speculating on where and how our forces or the enemy might strike next, now newspaper readers were economists, following the balance of payment figures, fretting at every increase in the inverse balance, welcoming every new export success. The "dollar gap" was as familiar a phrase to British people as the "Normandy beachhead" or the "Battle of the Atlantic" had been a few years earlier. Newspapers cheered every victory on the economic front and worried about every retreat.

Parliament passed a bill restoring the wartime direction of labor, so that people could be compelled to remain in an industry if it was deemed essential for national life. Attlee asked the miners to work extra hours without pay, and the unions to relax their opposition to foreign workers in factories. Dalton scolded the country for smoking too much – one-third more than before the war – since most of Britain's tobacco was imported from America. He appealed to people to cut their tobacco consumption by 25 percent as a patriotic duty. Smoking went down when he raised the duty on tobacco by 50 percent.

A group composed of representatives of the Treasury and other government departments put together a set of contingency plans in case no help came from America. It envisaged a situation that is almost unimaginable, a reduction to something like a Third World standard of living. One member of the committee wrote in an explanatory note: "The situation we are considering could be so desperate that all obligations, legal and moral, would have to be in the melting pot." A "famine-style food program" would be introduced.

People would be conscripted to work on the land and children taken from school to help bring in the harvest. Building would be drastically curtailed. Food would be so restricted that, according to one estimate, rations would be down to 1,700 calories a day, less than at any time during the war. "The country would have to withdraw from international trading agreements, breaching the terms of the American loan, and create a new trading bloc, including most of the Commonwealth," the report said.

Under this pressure, there were quarrels in the cabinet and several ministers threatened to resign on one issue or another. Cripps and Dalton even suggested a move to oust Attlee and put Bevin in his place, but Bevin, loyal to his chief, would not hear of it.

All through the year life in Britain became more and more constrained. The cars, radios, cutlery, and lawn mowers that Britain was producing were to be for export only; British people could not buy them. Restaurant meals, which were allowed to be no more than three courses, were cut to two, and if the diner had bread that would count as one of the courses. In July Eton College told parents that, because of the shortage of materials, top hats would no longer be required wearing for pupils until the present period of crisis had passed.

People were restricted in the amount of money they were allowed to spend abroad on holiday. In July the foreign travel allowance was cut from £75 a year to £35, to save foreign currency, and the following month it was reduced to zero. Thousands of continental holidays that had been booked were cancelled. The *Promenade des Anglais* in Nice, which was beginning to see tourists again, would have to do without *les Anglais*. Plans for an overseas honeymoon for Prince Philip and Princess Elizabeth were dropped.

Everyday life was harder than during the war, and British people did not have the morale-boosting sense which they had had in wartime that by their daily struggles they were holding an evil enemy at bay. As the author J. B. Priestly said in a broadcast: "Instead of feeling that we are together defying a vast dragon, we feel that our lives are being nibbled away by mice … Nothing generous is expected of us, so nothing generous emerges. We all accept the reason for austerity. But what a chilly, unimaginative world."

Britain's claim to be a regarded as a great power on a par with America died in the last week of June in 1947. At a series of meetings with Will Clayton, the British leaders asked for Britain to be a partner with America in the program for Marshall aid instead of being just one of the recipients. Clayton refused this.

Reading the record of these talks is painful. It is to see the desperate efforts of the British participants to retain their pride, to have it accepted that Britain, a country that still ruled the largest empire in the world, a country with global responsibilities, the only country to have fought the war from beginning to end, was a special country, not to be lumped together with all the Europeans, and to see these efforts fail before the brute facts of finance.

Clayton was accompanied at most of the meetings by the newly appointed American ambassador, Lewis Douglas. At the first meeting, at 10 Downing Street, Attlee, Bevin, Dalton, and Cripps were present. Bevin did most of the talking on the British side, arguing that Britain should not be bracketed together with other European countries. "Britain with its empire is on a different basis to the others," he insisted. He also said that Britain's parlous financial position put constraints on his foreign policy, so that at the Moscow conference he could not support Marshall as vigorously as he would have liked. "I think it would pay the United States and the world for the United States and the United Kingdom to establish a financial partnership," he said.

Clayton said he could not see the Administration going to Congress with new proposals for any one country. They must work out a European plan, he said. He added that Bevin's continued leadership would be welcome. How, he wanted to know, was Britain's problem different from that of other European countries? British ministers provided answers. Dalton said Britain was different because it was helping Germany. Cripps said another difference was Britain's extensive trade with non-European countries. Attlee said Britain had global responsibilities. He cited the decision to let Australian food supplies which were badly needed in Britain go to India instead to avoid starvation and catastrophe there. He said Britain took responsibility for India and for much of Africa as well.

Clayton insisted that if Britain were a partner in the aid program, receiving special assistance, this would violate the principle that there must be no piecemeal approach to the European problem. He added that even a non-piecemeal program would be difficult to sell to the public and to Congress. He threw in some criticism of Britain's management of its occupation zone in Germany. Attlee defended this vigorously, saying that socialist structures were being developed there which were alternatives to those created by the Nazis. He added that the giant industrial syndicates should not be allowed to re-emerge; if they were this would cause anxiety among Germany's neighbors. They talked about food. Clayton said the United States was exporting 15 million tons of cereal a year, and there was not the rail or sea transport to send more.

In the afternoon two senior civil servants argued that Britain was producing more than other European countries. If it were lumped together with the others this might put it last in line for aid, so it might do better staying out of the plan and doing bilateral deals. Clayton promised that there would be no "European pooling" that would take Britain down to the lowest level.

The next day Bevin remarked that Marshall aid might bring down the Iron Curtain. He said he had been cultivating Poland, and he thought Communist Yugoslavia would turn west because it needed things that Russia could not supply. He repeated that Britain and the British Empire could contribute to Europe's renewal. For Britain to go into the aid program and not contribute anything, he said, would be to sacrifice "the little bit of dignity we have left." Clayton stood firm. The two sides argued about American demands for closer integration of European economies and other free-trade arrangements.

In the end the British gave up on trying to get a special position. They worked out with Clayton a working paper on putting the aid program into operation which they were able to take to Paris. This stated that European nations should show why they were in such difficulties two years after the end of the war and what they intended to do about it.

The three-power meeting began in Paris on June 27. Molotov arrived in Paris accompanied by eighty-nine assistants and advisors, which indicated to the others that he was serious about participating in the plan. The French believed that some of these advisors were there to contact the French Communist Party.

Bidault opened with a statement in which he said that European nations must send America an account of Europe's position and its needs, and this should be completed by the beginning of September. "What is meant by Europe?" he asked, and then gave his answer: "In our view, it should include all countries of Europe, allies, ex-enemies or neutrals, with the provisional exception of Spain. All these European countries, in different degrees, are suffering from the same ills."

Getting down to practicalities right away, he laid out what proved to be the main lines of the conference that was to follow. He said the European countries should set up two studies, one to draw up a balance sheet of resources, the other to explore ways of increasing production. They should establish six committees to report on the main areas: agriculture, energy, transport, iron and steel, raw materials, and balance of payments. Each country would present the steering committee with a balance sheet of its own situation, its plans and its needs. All this would be coordinated with the newly formed Economic Commission for Europe, although, as he said, they would have to wait while the commission organized itself. Bevin seconded this proposal.

As Kennan and Bohlen had predicted, Molotov responded with anxieties about opening up Russia's economy for inspection. "Hitherto," he said, "it seemed perfectly clear that questions of internal sovereignty were a matter concerning the sovereignty of the peoples themselves, and that other countries should not interfere in such questions." He proposed that each country should submit its own list of requirements to the United States separately.

Bevin assured Molotov that no one intended to interfere with the sovereignty of participating countries. Molotov would not accept this. He said a single program for the European countries would mean the stronger powers imposing their will on the smaller countries and interfering in their internal affairs. He gave examples: Poland might be required to produce more coal while neglecting other industries, and Czechoslovakia to increase agricultural production at the expense of engineering. Bidault insisted that cooperation was necessary and gave the example of countries cooperating to win the war, which had not meant giving up any sovereignty.

It was clear now that there was going to be no agreement. Bidault proposed a compromise, which he knew Molotov would reject, in order to placate the French Communists. Although these were in opposition now, they were powerful and the Government always had to consider them. Molotov duly turned this down. As he spoke, Bevin leaned over to Piers Dixon, a senior Foreign Office official, and whispered, "This is the beginning of the Western bloc."

The Americans were relieved. They reckoned that a massive scheme to aid Europe including the Soviet Union would not get through Congress in the present international climate. Most of the Europeans were just as relieved. Bevin told the cabinet: "It's better to have them definitely out than half-heartedly in." He said that if the Soviet Union were a part of the Marshall Plan, it could make difficulties which would wreck the scheme. Soviet acceptance of the Marshall Plan is one of the might-have-beens of the twentieth century. If the Russians had participated it is doubtful whether the program would have gone ahead in anything like the form it did, and the history of the time would have been very different.

Poland had expressed an interest in Marshall aid, both through its ambassador in Washington and through contacts with the American Embassy in Warsaw. But Russia cracked the whip and all the Communist countries fell into line and denounced the plan. Czechoslovakia, which was not then a

Communist country but was an ally of the Soviet Union, said it would take part. It turned out that Moscow could crack the whip there also. The Prime Minister, Klement Gottwald, and the Foreign Minister, Jan Masaryk, visited Moscow and Stalin told them that participating in the plan would be regarded as an anti-Soviet act. The Czechs decided they could not afford to antagonize Russia and withdrew.

Bevin and Bidault issued an invitation to fourteen other European nations to join in setting up a new organization to respond to Marshall's suggestion, and tell America what help it wanted. All fourteen nations accepted the invitation.

The Clayton–Attlee talks in London were secret. Most Americans were still not fully aware during this time of the transformations that their Government was embarking on, and in particular the changing roles of the United States and Britain. But the men in the State Department were fully conscious of what was taking place.

Joseph Jones, who was in the State Department at the time, wrote an account of that spring and summer called *The Fifteen Weeks*. In it he said, in words which Dean Acheson later quoted approvingly:

> For reasons of high policy and good manners the United States did not, during the fifteen weeks, or thereafter, dramatise the takeover of leadership of the free world from Great Britain. It was not to our national interest at that critical moment to emphasize Britain's weakness in the Mediterranean and the Middle East, and good sportsmanship forbade noticing more than was necessary the exhaustion of a team mate. But during the fifteen weeks, the consciousness that a chapter in world history had come to an end was so real and ever-present as to be almost tangible.

The Marshall Plan, or the European Recovery Program, to give it its proper title, was more than just an aid program. It was a joint European–American program for restructuring the economies of western European countries and joining them more closely together, to set them on their feet, give them social and political stability, and make them once again trading partners on equal terms with the rest of the world. It achieved all of this. It also, with American pressure, sowed the seeds of the European Union.

It was quite different from previous aid programs in its aims and its conditions. It also included, at the European end, a few countries which had been neutral in the war and had not suffered directly, although every country's economy was affected. Switzerland had suffered no war damage and was an oasis of steaks and cream and comfort in the middle of Europe. But if there was to be a Europe-wide rearrangement these countries were going to be a part of it.

However, for a while it seemed possible that the European Recovery Program would never come into being. It depended on the European countries coming up with an agreed plan that would be acceptable to Washington, and at times during the summer of 1947 some doubted that they could achieve this.

Representatives of sixteen countries gathered in Paris on Saturday July 12, 1947, former allies, enemies, and neutrals. Germany was represented by officials of the Western occupying powers. All the countries of Europe west of what was now called the Iron Curtain were present, with the exception of Spain, which was a dictatorship. Although Portugal was also a dictatorship, it was represented at the conference because it had been a dictatorship for a long time and was a small country. Spain was a different matter. The Spanish ruler, General Franco, had overthrown Spanish democracy in a civil war that had ended only eight years before. The Spanish Civil War had engaged the passions of people around the world. To many, the continuation of the Franco regime was the unfinished business of the war against fascism. Franco's Spain was therefore not acceptable as a partner.

The countries taking part in the discussions were Austria, Belgium, Denmark, France, Greece, Iceland, Ireland, Italy, Luxembourg, the Netherlands, Norway, Portugal, Sweden, Switzerland, Turkey, and the United Kingdom. They set up the Committee of European Economic Cooperation, the CEEC, to produce a four-year recovery program to be supported by requests for US aid. Their first act was to send a message to Washington formally accepting General Marshall's offer. Bevin thought Bidault suspected him of trying to take over the process, so the two men agreed that the committee would meet in Paris but would have a British chairman. They would meet all summer and present their program by the beginning of September. The chairman was to be Sir Oliver Franks, a philosophy professor and provost of an Oxford college turned wartime civil servant, who turned out to be an excellent choice.

The committee institutionalized the division of Europe. The countries of western Europe were members and no others. It also institutionalized the idea of Europe. These countries had never before joined together to cooperate, in economics or anything else. Now each country was required to draw up and share with the others a balance sheet of its resources and needs. It was a formidable undertaking.

CHAPTER FIVE

INVENTING EUROPE

The Committee for European Economic Cooperation met in Paris throughout the summer of 1947. Never before had representatives of all the principal countries of western Europe met to work out a plan that would affect all their economies. For a while things did not go well.

Their main task was drawing up the lists and working out the sums. But there were other issues to thrash out. For example, how much aid should they ask for in commodities and how much in cash? They would be receiving things from America, paid for by the US Government; could they ask for dollars to spend elsewhere? Britain bought wheat and beef from Argentina. If it had no dollars for this purpose it would have to send coal to Argentina and not to Europe, yet British coal was to be a part of any European recovery program. Could it spend Marshall aid dollars in Argentina? Could some of the aid go to colonies, in particular France's North African colonies? What was the position of countries that were neutral and had suffered no war damage?

The CEEC set up an executive committee and this bred other committees, specializing in different areas, as Bidault had proposed earlier. Will Clayton, as the begetter of the program, went over to Paris, and spent most of the summer there. He told the parties that they had to produce a program that was acceptable to the Administration and to Congress. He stressed this, and explained the intricacies of executive–Congress relations and the politics of Congress. He said they must show that the aid program would make them self-sufficient and not leave them needing more. They also had to take steps to integrate their economies, and at the least establish a customs union.

Pressure for European integration was to be a constant theme in US policy. It seemed to Americans to be common sense that the European continent would be better off if its countries were to join together, as the American states had joined together. At the very least they should open their borders to trade so that they would have the advantage of a single market for their products, which the United States enjoyed. Some compared the situation with that of the thirteen American colonies in the aftermath of the War of Independence, joining together to form the United States, and envisaged a United States of

Europe. This comparison took little note of the different cultures, languages, and histories of European countries.

Later in the summer, when it became clear that the committee was not making much progress, Clayton was joined by others to reinforce his strictures about what would and would not be acceptable. Jefferson Caffery, the American ambassador in Paris, sat in on the talks some of the time, and Ambassador Lewis Douglas commuted from London; later George Kennan and Paul Nitze went over from Washington.

The sixteen member countries submitted to the committee their separate shopping lists, something that was not supposed to happen. The Americans saw sixteen countries pursuing separate national goals. General Marshall, reviewing the reports he was receiving from Paris, wrote that "elements of mutual aid and the subordination of national aims to a co-operative approach has been generally lacking." As for Britain, that country, it seemed, "wishes to benefit from a European program while not being wholly a European power.

Kennan wrote a report which concluded that the Europeans would not come up with a plan that met Clayton's requirements. He said the participants were each acting in their own interests and treating one another "with old world cordiality," which means that no one questioned anyone else's figures, partly because they felt their own were vulnerable to challenge. He went on, not without sympathy: "It would be wrong to laugh at this gingerly approach or to put it all down to short-sighted timidity. It reflects serious European realities which must be taken into account."

Kennan was certainly right about the fragility of some of the figures. Sir Eric Roll, one of the British team, noticed one night that Greek officials were working late filling in some questionnaires. He told them, "But these are not for you, these are to be sent home to Athens for the people there to fill in." They told him that the officials in Athens did not know the answers about the Greek economy any more than they did, so they were making up the figures.

The United States had said Europeans should form a customs union. Sir Oliver Franks asked Clayton whether this was a precondition for American aid. Clayton said it was not a precondition but it would greatly improve the chances of acceptance by Congress. So the Executive Committee set up another committee to investigate the idea. Their report when it came was hardly a clarion call. It said the idea of a customs union "contains important possibilities for the future of Europe ... and the problems involved should receive careful and detailed study." So they set up a Customs Union Study Group. But studying the subject was not much of an advance on discussing it.

When it came to Germany, politics clashed with economics. Economically, Europeans needed German revival; politically they feared it. Germany could produce the things that European industry needed as it had before the war: machinery, metals, chemicals, coal, steel. But the European allies still wanted to ensure that Germany could never again have the ability to wage war, and heavy industries such as these could make it powerful. It was a dilemma for France in particular. Any suggestion by the Government that it might agree to an increase in German steel production, or any step toward a central German authority, was met by cries of betrayal, most loudly of all by the Communists. Bidault pleaded with the other governments to desist from public statements about German revival, which would only make it more difficult for him. In the end the CEEC report accepted the revival of German industry, but only after a struggle. As was stated by a report to the US Administration entitled *European Recovery and American Aid* by a commission headed by Clark Clifford, the White House counsel: "There were strong economic and financial pressures in all the countries including the United States pushing against political objections to the idea of strengthening Germany."

Under-Secretary of State Lovett, like his boss Marshall, was worried about the way things were going in Paris. He wanted the report completed by the beginning of September so that Congress could debate it and approve it in its current session. But as the summer went on it became clear that this was not likely to happen, and Lovett cabled Clayton: "Realistic and workable program more important than reaching deadline for report."

The summer in Europe was unusually hot and dry. While the CEEC members talked, crops were dying in the drought-ridden French countryside and cattle were being slaughtered prematurely because there was no feed for them. Meat was rare and butchers in Paris were allowed to open only at weekends. Even at the priciest restaurants which bought their food on the black market diners would be lucky to get decent meat. The delegates sometimes had to stop work in the evening because there was no electric light.

In Washington also, committees were meeting. Truman set up three including legislators of both parties to consider aid. If the plan went ahead a massive amount would be requested from Congress later in the year and he was preparing the ground. The first committee, under Averell Harriman, who was now Secretary of Commerce, was to consider how America could help European recovery. The second, under Secretary of the Interior Julius Krug, considered America's resources and foreign aid, and the third, under Edwin G. Nourse, the Chairman of the Council of Economic Advisors, considered the impact of foreign aid on the domestic economy. All three reported at the end of the summer and all their reports were positive: they found that America had the resources to help Europe and doing so would not damage the domestic economy. This was what Truman expected them to conclude, indeed what he intended that they should. As Loy Henderson admitted later, they were "stacked committees."

The House of Representatives sent a nineteen-member study group under Massachusetts congressman Christian Herter on a tour of Europe. Herter, unlike the other committee members, had a cosmopolitan background. He had been born in Paris, the son of an expatriate American artist, and he had served at the American Embassy in Berlin in 1916 and on the US delegation to the Versailles Peace Conference. (He later became Secretary of State under President Eisenhower.) Usually, congressional trips abroad include a certain amount of junketing but Herter insisted that this should be a working trip with no time out for entertainment. Committee members were not to bring wives along. He was a hard taskmaster. On the journey across on the liner *Queen Mary* they had three-hour briefing sessions from State Department officials in the morning and afternoon.

Their first stop was London, where they had tea with Attlee and Bevin. Bevin told the committee that if they wanted to save Britain and particularly continental Europe from disaster, they must send help before Christmas. He stressed as he did on other occasions the precarious situation on the continent, and said that unless France received help Britain might have a Communist neighbor across the Channel. The warning was echoed by Bidault when the American delegation saw him in Paris. The committee members talked to ministers and economic officials in one country after another, moving at a rapid pace. One member said, "We tried to look at Europe in about the way a banker would look at a bankrupt corporation trying to get a loan."

Other American legislators visited Europe that summer. As a member of Will Clayton's staff recalled, "Almost every Congressional committee that could think of an excuse to come over to Europe came over. Within six weeks we had about 15 groups visit. Clayton met with as many as he could and gave them his views." One group, the Smith–Mundt Committee, investigated the information effort and visited Communist capitals as well as Western ones for briefings by embassy officials. In Paris Bidault told everyone that there was a desperate battle in France between Communists and non-Communists. In Berlin General Clay told them that he was sure the Russians were not planning war and were not ready for it.

Altogether 215 members of Congress, including the Herter mission crossed the Atlantic flying from capital to capital in US military aircraft. Embassy officials were kept busy briefing them and arranging appointments for them and catering to their travel needs. Most skeptics among the visitors were converted to the need for aid. In some cases at least, their experiences took in more than the diplomatic circuit. Several members were so moved by the hungry Germans they met that they gave them chocolates, soap, and even clothes, and took addresses and promised to send food parcels when they got home.

Not all the delegates were so sympathetic, nor were they always well received. Congressman John Taber, a conservative Republican from Ohio, was doubtful about aid and kept saying he had not seen starving people. In Britain he met the Minister for Fuel, Hugh Gaitskell, at lunch and told him Britain was making a better effort to recover than most European countries. Gaitskell, who liked most of the Americans he met, did not like Taber. He wrote in his diary, "It is pretty intolerable to accept patronizing comments from people who are quite so odious."

The Herter Committee produced a report that was thoughtful and insightful. It foresaw the need for cooperation among the Marshall aid recipients but also the limit of the American power to impose this. It concluded:

> If we undertake the proposed European recovery program, we are in effect assuming the responsibility for the economic revival of Western Europe. Responsibility without power is a situation generally avoided by cautious people. But the alternative in terms of human lives, human misery and human slavery is perhaps too frightful to permit us the luxury of being cautious. We can only hope that the nations of Western Europe, who have the power over their own economic destinies, will themselves realize the responsibilities of their predicament and, by actively co-operating with each other, help themselves.

The CEEC completed a draft plan for Marshall aid in early September. It called for $29 billion of aid over four years. It estimated the trade imbalance with America at $19.9 billion. It said: "The participating countries have sought to reduce their needs from the American continent to a minimum." Even so, Clayton said this figure was too high, that Congress would never allow it. He told them to go back and try again.

The CEEC reduced the amount to $20.6 billion, then, after more conversations and another attack on the shopping list, to $17 billion. Two key items it asked for, the first essentials for European recovery, were coal and nitrogen fertilizer, the first to raise the level of industry, the second that of agriculture. The Europeans promised that they would work toward reducing tariff barriers and a common policy for energy. This was a nod to the State Department's pressure for closer economic integration, but it did not commit them to anything.

The report consisted of two parts, an 86-page general report and a 355-page volume that contained the reports of the four subcommittees. These set out Europe's plight. They did not break it down into requests for aid for individual countries. Sir Oliver Franks took it to Washington and on September 22nd he presented it to the Administration. As *Time* magazine reported admiringly, "To a spellbound conference of U.S. officials, Franks put on a show they have never forgotten. He talked for two-and-a-half hours on the whole European recovery program without notes, pause or repetition."

The report had to be considered by the Administration and then by Congress, which was not then in session, a process that would take months. But events would not wait on this. In October France ran right out of dollars and had none to buy coal or wheat, both of which it needed urgently. The International Monetary Fund allowed France to take out $93 million in credit, and the US Government stepped in by repaying in dollars some debts the Army had accrued from stationing troops in France.

In September the President's Advisory Committee decided that while some countries such as the United Kingdom had resources, although they were declining rapidly, France and Italy had now "reached the bottom of the barrel." Several Democratic congressmen who had been to Europe in the summer, seeing this report, said there should be a special session of Congress to deal with this situation. Congress was not due to meet until January. Truman let the pressure build up, and then called a special session of Congress on October 23. He asked for $642 million in interim aid for France, Italy, and Austria.

This was none too soon. France was swept by a wave of strikes accompanied by violence that bordered on insurrection. The Communists, out of the Government and now swinging into opposition, led the strikes. They were exploiting real anger. People were suffering hardship. In the mining towns of the north men came out on the streets and threw broken-up paving stones at police, and troops were sent in. In Marseilles strikers seized the town hall and beat up the Mayor. Strikers sabotaged a train going from Paris to strike-hit Lille which they thought carried riot police, and sixteen passengers were killed. Two million people were on strike in December, a million tons of coal were lost and most of the ports were closed. The strikes added to the shortages, with frequent cuts in power supply and in food deliveries.

America intervened in France covertly. With the help of Irving Brown, the European representative of the American Federation of Labor, it funneled money to the new trade union group that rejected Communist leadership, the Force Ouvrière. From now on the American Government financed in secret groups in France opposing the Communists. It supported not right-wing groups but the liberal left. It was aiming to deprive the Communists of the leadership of the forces working for change. Lovett wrote to Caffery: "Politically speaking, the break must come to the left, or at the very least in the middle, of the Socialist Party."

Italians also were suffering hardship. Farm output in Italy was down by more than 20 percent because of the drought and a farm workers' strike. The average diet was down to 2,000 calories a day. There also the Communists exploited grievances, leading strikes and mob action and moving away from their conciliatory parliamentary role. The party brought 20,000 former partisans in trains and buses to Rome for a congress of the National Partisans' Association. These marched through the city in military formation, watched by the association's guest of honor, a Soviet general. They were unarmed, but the menace was clear.

The Administration told Congress that the situation in those countries was desperate. In committee hearings, Marshall, Harriman, and Lovett all stressed the danger that Communism would follow economic collapse. There were a few objections. Some including Taft wanted the aid sum reduced to $400 million. Vandenberg said this would be like "throwing a 15-foot rope to a man who is drowning 20 feet off shore." Because goods as well as money would be sent, some congressmen from farm states wanted an amendment saying fertilizers and grain should not be sent if these were in short supply in America. This was defeated. Others uttered the cry that was always heard at this time when aid to Europe was being discussed, "What about China?" – for in China the Communists were gaining ground in the civil war. Conservative Republicans were isolationist on Europe but interventionist on Asia.

On December 15 Congress voted for $522 million for France, Italy, and Austria, and $18 million for China. The latter was hardly more than a gesture since a sum that small was not going to make a difference in China's situation.

Four days later, Truman placed before Congress the European Recovery Program. This was the big one. It was known generally now as the Marshall Plan and Truman was content that it should be so. As he told Clark Clifford,

"Can you imagine its chances of passage in an election year in a Republican Congress if it was called the Truman Plan?"

In London *The Times* said in an editorial the following day: "The year 1947 will be known as the year of the Marshall Plan. Mr. Truman's presidency will be remembered for the program of aid to Europe presented to Congress yesterday."

The Marshall Plan was not simply an act of national generosity. It was vitally important for America that Europe recover. If Europe remained poor and could not buy American products, the American economy would be crippled. If Europe became Communist America would be beleaguered and threatened.

This was made clear in a report by the State Department/Army/Navy Coordinating Committee at this time. The report said that in 1947 America could expect to export $7.5 billion in goods and services more than it imported, but foreign countries could not continue to pay for these. It went on: "The conclusion is inescapable that under present programs and policies the world will not be able to buy U.S. exports at the 1946–47 rate beyond another 12–18 months ... A substantial decline in the US export surplus would have a depressing effect on business activity and employment."

This was not something new. Since 1900 if not before, American factories and American farms had produced more than Americans could consume. This was a driving force behind American expansion during the imperialist period of the 1900s. President Woodrow Wilson said in 1914: "Our industries have expanded to such a point that they will burst their jackets if they cannot find free outlets in the markets of the world. Our domestic markets no longer suffice. We need foreign markets."

President Roosevelt, during the Depression, had hit the same theme. "Foreign markets have to be regained if American producers are to rebuild a full and enduring domestic prosperity for our people. There is no other way if we would avoid painful economic dislocation, social readjustments and unemployment." In 1944 Dean Acheson, then Assistant Secretary of the Treasury, told Congress: "We cannot have full employment and prosperity in the United States without foreign markets." This was the message of his speech to the Delta Council in Mississippi in March. Throughout the twentieth century American administrations argued for a free-trade world. As a result of congressional pressure, however, America did not always practise what it preached and erected tariff barriers time and time again.

In the drive to help Europe recover, historic ties and national sentiments also played a role. To ignore these and see only national self-interest would be as simplistic as it would be to see only disinterested generosity. The United States was more Europe-focused in 1947 than it is today. The country's center of gravity was further to the east. California had half the population it has today, even though it had doubled during the war. Apart from Afro-Americans, there was no sizeable ethnic group that did not come from Europe. It was an America in which Paul G. Hoffman, the industrialist who would direct the Marshall Plan, could say with confidence, addressing the Foreign Trade Convention: "The 270 million people of the Marshall Plan nations are essentially good people. That must be obvious, because they are your ancestors and mine." The make-up of America at this time, with its dominant group of northern European origins, was due to the immigration laws of 1921 and 1924, which set out to keep the ethnic balance of the United States the same as it had been in 1890. The country-by-country quota system discriminated against southern Europeans and even more against Asians and Africans. Immigration law was changed in 1960.

There was a lot of goodwill among Americans toward Europe. People continued to contribute to CARE packages. As a stunt to dramatize aid for Europe's hungry, a Friendship Train set out from Hollywood in November 1947, seen off by film stars, to cross the country collecting donations along the way. Schools, churches, and community groups contributed. When it arrived in New York just before Christmas it had collected 12,120 tons of food in its 266 freight cars to be shipped to Europe. Packages contained condensed milk, wheat, flour, and a soya product called all-purpose food. Between 1945 and 1949, private American donors gave more than $500 million in aid to Europe.

The East Coast Establishment played a larger part in government than it does today, and this was Atlantic centered and culturally Anglophile. Members of this Establishment went to the same private schools. Groton was the favored school of this upper class, as Eton and Harrow are of the British upper class. (It is correctly pronounced "Grotton" and students past and present are known as "Grotties.") Like the British public (meaning private) schools on which it modeled itself, it aimed to imbue its students with an ethos of service to go with their privilege. Usually they went on to Ivy League colleges. Some members of this Establishment were what Washington calls in-and-outers, moving, once they had achieved a level of success, between private careers, which usually meant Wall Street or the law, and government. They were mostly Republicans, conservative politically and socially, but many served in Democratic administrations. Like their British counterparts, they were raised with the sense that they had a duty to serve, and also a right to govern.

Some past and present members of the Truman Administration were members of this Establishment. Acheson and Harriman had rowed together at Groton. Harriman and Lovett had known each other since childhood and were at Yale together, and they were fellow-members at Yale of the elite Skull and Bones club. Stimson was also a member of Skull and Bones at Yale. John McCloy was a fellow-director with Harriman and Lovett of the Union Pacific Railroad.

These were people who would be at home in a London club as they would in their own clubs in New York and Washington. Theirs was a horizontal affinity, class speaking to class. They were familiar with Europe. Harriman, the son of a railway magnate, who was ambassador to Moscow during the war, first visited Russia at the age of eight when Czar Nicholas was on the throne. Europe for them was not, as it was for many Americans, a collection of countries a long way away which they could forget about once they had passed their high school history and geography exams. They knew its capital cities, they had social contacts there. (Roosevelt, a graduate of Groton and Harvard with a wealthy family background, was also a member of this class and visited Europe from an early age, but he distanced himself from his class politically with his liberal policies.)

These men knew each other's wives and families and socialized together. They thrashed out foreign policy, along with a few other government figures and sometimes a very few selected journalists, in their own living rooms. In 1914–17 and in 1940–1, they had worked to associate America with Britain's war effort. They were regarded by Midwestern isolationists with deep suspicion as tainted by their European connections and insufficiently patriotic. Now, once again, they threw their weight on the side of aid to Europe.

The Administration's acceptance of the CEEC plan was one step in the process. Congress still had to be persuaded. The State Department, sometimes working with members of the CEEC, turned the report into a workable program that could be put before Congress. Statistical data for every country and projections of aid and its effect had to be tabulated. For the men involved it was an exciting project, putting a whole continent back on its feet. They felt like military men in time of war, aware that now their time has come and the country needs them. One man working on the project, Lincoln Gordon, writing about that time later, recalled "a sense of excitement and dedication. Here was a cause akin to winning World War Two."

It was also an exacting project, involving a wealth of detail. Paul Nitze, who headed it, borrowed all the calculating machines of the Prudential Life Insurance Company of Newark, New Jersey. They were working in a chaotic physical environment, because the State Department was being moved, office by office, filing cabinet by filing cabinet, from the nineteenth-century building on Pennsylvania Avenue to the vast new air-conditioned building in the Foggy Bottom area of Washington which it occupies today. They worked through the Christmas holidays while Congress was in recess. Sometimes they labored day and night to get reports completed. One man stayed at his desk through the night and, driving home exhausted in the morning, crashed his car. His colleagues, knowing the dedication that lay behind this, each chipped in fifty dollars toward the expense of the repairs.

Then the drive got under way to sell the Marshall Plan to Congress and to the American public. 1948 was an election year, for most members of Congress and for the President, and senators and congressmen were likely to be more attentive than usual to what their constituents were saying.

The State Department mounted a massive public information program. It sent out speakers and produced radio spots. General Marshall lent his prestige. He went on a speaking tour, beginning with the Pittsburgh Chamber of Commerce and the Cotton Council in Atlanta. To business groups he said America's prosperity depended on the recovery of international trade. To farmers he talked of the commodities which America was producing in surplus that Europe needed. He found talking to women's groups particularly rewarding. "My goodness, they went back home and they scared Congress to death in the next 24 hours," he said later. "You never saw such rapid action in your life. Men's groups listen but they don't do anything." The National Association of Manufacturers came out in support of the plan, for it was going to be good for business. So did the American Bar Association, the General Federation of Women's Clubs, and the Veterans of Foreign Wars.

A Citizens' Committee for the Marshall Plan was created, with covert State Department backing. Dean Acheson was now a private citizen. He had resigned to go back into private law practise; he had intended to do so earlier but when Marshall became Secretary of State he said he would stay on for six months to ease the transition. He became one of the directors of the Citizens' Committee. The other director was Robert Patterson, the former Secretary for War. The President was Henry L. Stimson, who had been the grand old man of the Truman Administration. The East Coast Establishment was well represented and, appropriately, the committee held its inaugural meeting at the Harvard Club in New York. But they made sure industry was represented, and labor also, in the person of James Cafey of the Congress of Industrial Organization, who was on the Executive Council. This was similar to an earlier citizens' committee, the Committee to Defend America by Aiding the Allies, which had pressed for aid to Britain in 1940–1, before the United States entered the war. That committee had also campaigned independently for Administration policies. The similarity is not surprising; many of the leading members were the same.

The committee took out full-page advertisements in New York's two leading newspapers and it organized petitions that collected 200,000 signatures. Its members fanned out across the country and addressed meetings and appeared on radio programs. They worked with other groups supporting Marshall aid such as the National Farmers' Union, and helped them prepare their testimony before Congress. The committee even produced a comic book called *Who's Against the Marshall Plan*.

Stimson wrote an article about the Marshall Plan in the journal *Foreign Affairs* in which he said: "The reconstruction of Western Europe is a task from which Americans can decide to stand apart only if they wish to desert every principle which they claim to hold dear." The committee reprinted 100,000 copies of this and distributed them. Will Clayton, now out of government, went on speaking tours. The committee carried out a carefully directed campaign targeted at members of Congress, singling out those who were doubtful and who could be converted, blitzing their constituencies with pro-Marshall Plan propaganda and speeches.

Truman did not play a prominent part in this campaign. He thought his presence at the head would make it a partisan issue, the same reason that he had insisted it be called the Marshall Plan and not the Truman Plan. But he helped keep Europe's plight in the public eye by setting up a Citizens' Food Committee to save food so that it could be sent as aid, with a leading business figure, Charles Luckmann, the CEO of Lever Brothers as its president. Its members wrote articles and appeared on radio programs. It called for the public to observe eggless Mondays and meatless Tuesdays, and asked restaurants not to serve bread unless a customer asked for it. By this sort of measure they aimed to save a million bushels of wheat.

The push to sell it to Congress was not going to be easy. This was a Republican Congress, and it had been elected on a promise to cut government spending. Members were going to have to face their constituents and explain why, with the war over for two years, some of their tax dollars were going to Europe. So far as most of them were concerned, America had already sacrificed a lot of its sons for the cause of European freedom, and they did not expect to be asked to give more now. Charles Halleck of Indiana, the majority leader in the House, warned Truman, "There is a growing resistance to these programs. I have been out on the hustings and I know people don't like it." Republicans were all too aware that they had promised the voters before the election that they would cut government spending and government activity, that they would "Get the government out of your pockets and off your backs." The Washington correspondent of Britain's *New Statesman*, Richard Strout, told his readers: "The lack of enthusiasm over the country as a whole is now a major factor."

There is a natural tension between the State Department and congressmen. The State Department looks outward, at America's relations with the rest of the world. A member of Congress looks to his constituency. His constituents want to know how a measure will affect their lives and their livelihood, what's in it for them, and the congressman or senator has to address himself to this.

To wage the campaign in Congress over the Marshall aid bill, the usual State Department machinery was not enough: the big artillery was moved up. Ambassador Lewis Douglas, who was a former congressman, was brought back from London to head the European Recovery Program Committee, which was to manage the Administration's overall effort. Charles Bohlen was made the head of congressional liaison. He said later that during the next few months he saw more of members of Congress than he saw of his wife.

Marshall was also prevailed upon to cultivate senators, which did not come naturally to this upright figure. Bohlen said, "Politicians were a race that Marshall got along with but did not understand. Their motivation mystified him." His Under-Secretary, Robert Lovett, was socially more pliable and better at it. He developed a particularly close relationship with Vandenberg. Lovett would stop off at Vandenberg's apartment in the Wardman Park Hotel, the residential building at the highest point in Washington geographically and socially, several times a week for cocktails and political chat. Sometimes he would break the rules and bring with him classified State Department cables about Communist activities in western Europe.

The hard work that embassies in Europe had put in the previous summer entertaining visiting members of Congress paid off. Most of those who went to Europe came back persuaded of the need for an aid program. Congressman Richard Nixon, who was in the Herter group, found that 75 percent of his constituents in Southern California were against Marshall aid. Nonetheless, he spoke out in favor and promised his constituents, many of them orange farmers, that he would press for oranges to be included in the aid. Senator

Everett Dirksen was an influential Republican and a longtime isolationist, and his Illinois constituents were startled to hear him stumping the state for aid for Europe.

The State Department was worried that Congress, while not actually rejecting the bill, might whittle it down, reducing the sums available and imposing restrictive conditions. Writing to his wife Bess at home in Missouri, Truman vented his frustration with congressional haggling over the amounts involved. In a letter, written on White House stationery in his sloping handwriting, he complained, "In October and November 1945 I cancelled 63 billions in appropriations, 55 billions in one crack. Our war cost in that year was set at 105 billions. This 16½ billion is a four-year period and this is for *peace*."

The Senate Foreign Relations Committee began hearings in January 1948 in the marble caucus room in the Senate Office Building. Ninety-five witnesses appeared before the committee, government officials and leaders in many areas of American life, and it took seventy-six written statements. For the Administration, the testimony on the interim aid bill had been a dress rehearsal.

General Marshall was the first witness. Facing a battery of press cameras and microphones, he assured the committee that the measure was in America's interest, and he gave two reasons. One was strategic: "If we don't give this aid we will face a Europe of police states, and our defense costs will rise." The other was economic: The consequences of failure to carry through the aid program, he said, would be to confront America, "if not with a trade barrier, certainly with a great detriment to our ordinary business, or commerce and trade." Anticipating arguments over the amount, Marshall said, "An inadequate program would involve a wastage of our resources with an ineffective result. Either undertake to meet the requirements of the problem or don't undertake it at all."

Averell Harriman and Bernard Baruch followed him, testifying that Marshall aid was essential. The strategic rationale, the threat of Communism, predominated, although it was usually referred to obliquely. Harriman and Forrestal both said that, if the aid program did not go through, the Administration would have to ask immediately for increased defense expenditure, without specifying who they would be defending against. Business leaders testified. Vandenberg as usual raised the issue to a higher plane. "The greatest nation on earth either justifies or surrenders its leadership. We must choose," he said.

When it came to the nitty-gritty of the program, the State Department hit the committee with twenty-six brown books, categorizing aid under ninety-two headings. One senator congratulated them on the thoroughness of the information provided but complained, "It's a magnificent piece of work but it's inches thick."

Witnesses stressed the theme of European integration. Lewis Douglas told the Senate committee that the Europeans should create "the type of economic federal union that we now have in the United States." Marshall, Harriman, and Forrestal all said European integration was "one of the most important considerations in the program."

In the House of Representatives, the Appropriations Committee was headed by John Taber of Ohio, whose European trip had not persuaded him of the need for help. He questioned Paul Nitze about the brown books volume by volume with a doggedness that amounted to harassment. The nit-picking reached its apogee when the subject of pulse peas, listed in one of the brown books, came up and he forced Paul Nitze to admit that he did not know a lot about the cultivation of pulse peas. He complained that the people behind the program were not sufficiently informed. Lovett called Taber and reminded him that he was the committee's authority on defense appropriations and asked him, "Do you know how many rivets there are in the wing of a B-29 bomber?" Taber saw the point and backed down.

State Department figures gave their all. David Lilienthal, then Chairman of the Atomic Energy Commission, records an evening meeting in his diary: "Lovett was supposed to be here; as we gathered Edmund Guillon came in to say, 'Mr. Lovett has just returned from all day on the Hill. He asks to be excused; he is dead tired and is going home to bed.' Kennan looked up and said, 'It has been ghastly. I'm afraid if he ever goes to bed he'll never get up.'"

The Administration was in a hurry to get the bill through, partly because some countries needed help urgently, and partly because it wanted the aid to start flowing before the Italian elections scheduled for April 18, which the Communists were given a good chance of winning. So the fear of Communism was ramped up. This was done with a message from Berlin. The head of Army intelligence, General John Chamberlain, told General Clay in Berlin that he was worried about the lack of preparedness for war. Clay responded with a telegram saying:

> For many months, based on logical analysis, I have felt and held that war was unlikely for at least ten years. Within the last few weeks I have felt a subtle change in the Soviet attitude which I cannot define but which now gives me a feeling that it may come with dramatic suddenness. I cannot support this change in my own thinking with any data or outward evidence

> in relationships other than to describe it as a feeling of a new tenseness in every Soviet individual which whom we have official relations. I am unable to submit any official report in the absence of supporting evidence but my feeling is real.

The message was private but it was passed around Washington and key senators and congressmen saw it or at least knew about it. The Senate Committee passed the bill on to the Senate.

In February 1948 the Communists seized power in Czechoslovakia and ended democracy in that country. This rammed home the idea of a Communist threat more than any message by an American general could do.

Czechoslovakia was an ally of the Soviet Union. Having been betrayed by the West at Munich, it had decided to opt for an ally closer at hand. Soviet troops had liberated Prague but, unlike in the Balkan capitals, they had left. Czechoslovakia was independent and it was a Western-style democracy with a democratic history. In the last elections, held in 1946, the Communists won 38 percent of the votes and a socialist party allied to them another 13 percent. In 1948 there was a coalition government with a Communist prime minister but a non-Communist president and a majority of non-Communists.

The Communist Minister of the Interior began packing the police force with his men. The other members of the cabinet tried to get the President, Eduard Beneš, to stop him. When Beneš refused they resigned in protest, expecting a cabinet reshuffle. But the Communists, fortified by the presence of Soviet Deputy Foreign Minister Valerian Zorin, who had flown in a few days earlier, sent their militia into the streets, closed down other political parties, put down opposition demonstrations, and browbeat Beneš, who was unwell, into giving them formal power. There was an election three months later with only one list of candidates.

The Czech statesman best known in the West was Jan Masaryk, the Foreign Minister. The son of the Czechoslovak Republic's first President, he was the head of the wartime Government-in-Exile and a staunch democrat. Two weeks after the coup, his pajama-clad body was found in the street under his apartment. The Communist Government said it was suicide, but his friends said this was unlikely. Most people thought he had been murdered.

In western Europe defeatism was in the air. In the wake of defeat in the war, there was an almost mesmerizing power in the claim of Communism that it was the wave of the future, that history was on its side. Georges Bidault told David Bruce, the American ambassador, "A fear psychosis saps the will to resist the Communist offensive and the very strength of Western European

The Labour Party comes to power in Britain. Labour leader Clement Attlee with cheering supporters.

Tanks in the London streets. The Victory Parade.

Shopping, 1946. The average British housewife spent an hour a day queuing.

In America, industry turned from making weapons to consumer goods, and advertisements heralded an age of prosperity.

Cord Meyer with Albert Einstein, who supported his campaign for world government.

Germans line up for rations of soup in what was once a main shopping street in Hamburg.

Ernest Bevin, British Foreign Secretary.

Dean Acheson, US Under-Secretary of State (later Secretary of State).

Clearing away snowdrifts in Britain's disastrous winter of 1947. Snow like this had never been seen before.

Communists clash with police in Paris as the country is swept by disorder.

Pro-Zionists demonstrate against Britain in New York.

George F. Kennan, architect of the containment policy.

British film star Margaret Lookwood wearing Dior's New Look, its longer, fuller skirt and frivolous hemline looking to an end of wartime austerity.

Secretary of State George Marshall testifying before the Senate.

Communist meeting in Italy's crucial election campaign. The Communists seemed the likely winners.

Sept. 30, 1947.

THE WHITE HOUSE
WASHINGTON

Dear Bess:- Yesterday was one of the most hectic of days as I told you. I'm not sure what has been my worst day. But here is a situation fraught with terrible consequences. Suppose, for instance that Italy should fold up and that Tito then would march into the Po Valley. All the Mediterranean Coast of France then is open to Russian occupation and the iron curtain comes to Bordeaux, Callais, Antwerp and the Hague. We withdraw from Greece and Turkey and prepare for war! It just must not happen. But here I am confronted with a violently opposition Congress whose committees

Truman vents his concerns about Europe in a letter to his wife, Bess, back home in Independence.

The first ship carrying Marshall aid arrives at the French port of Bordeaux, to be received with a ceremony.

An airlift keeps the lifeline to Berlin open despite the Soviet blockade.

President Truman with his wife and daughter campaigning for re-election.

peoples." In Italy some middle-class people were joining the Communist Party as insurance. Nancy Mitford, the British writer living in Paris, wrote to Evelyn Waugh, a month after the Prague coup, that she was working on another book, but went on: "What's the point of my getting on with it when the Russians will be here ... Thank God for having no children. I can take the pill and say goodbye." When China became Communist and followed a more radical path even than Russia, a joke went: "There are optimists and pessimists. The optimists are learning Russian, the pessimists are learning Chinese."

There was a *fin de siècle* strain abroad. One could not see much confidence that Europe and its culture would rise again. That Nazism, with its creed of blood and soil, should have triumphed in Germany, the most educated country on the continent, seemed to many to represent a moral defeat for the liberal values of the Enlightenment, and its conquest of the rest of Europe underlined this defeat. Europe did not liberate itself from Nazism, it was liberated from outside. The advance of the Soviet armies and the postwar upsurge of Communism at home further sapped morale.

Defeatism was seen in some of the literature of the time, the novels of Malaparte and Cesar Pavese in Italy and in France in the novels and plays of Sartre, Camus, and Simone de Beauvoir, which reflect, not despair, as was sometimes said, but an abandonment of any idea of seeking strength in social or political values. The leading British literary magazine *Horizon* ceased publication in February 1948 with a sigh of renunciation. "It is closing-time in the gardens of the West, and from now on an artist will be judged only by the resonance of his solitude or the quality of his despair," it said in its final editorial.

It seemed that Europe and its liberal traditions had had their day. There was a new force coming from the east, not handsome, perhaps, but strong and confident, and it seemed that this was the bull that, as in the myth, would carry off the maiden Europa.

In Washington the aid bill passed from the committee stage to the full Senate on March 1. Senator Vandenberg as the majority leader introduced it, speaking to a packed chamber. He started with an oblique reference to Czechoslovakia and the threat of Communism: "The exposed frontiers of hazard move almost hourly to the west." Then he spoke about Europe's place in the world and its meaning for America. "Within the purview of this plan," he said,

> are 270 million people of the stock which has largely made America. These are 26 percent of all the literate of the earth. Before the war they operated 68

> percent of all the ships that sailed the sea. They grew 27 percent of all the world's cereals. They produced 37 percent of the world's steel. They sold 24 percent of the world's exports and bought 39 percent of the world's imports. They are struggling, against great and ominous odds, to regain their feet. They must not be allowed to fail.

He spoke for an hour and twenty minutes about the work that had gone into the Marshall Plan, shaking his head for emphasis from time to time so that his few strands of hair bobbed about, and concluded at his most solemn: "This can be the turning point in history for a hundred years to come. If it fails we will have done our best. If it succeeds, our children and our children's children will call us blessed." He sat down to a standing ovation.

Vandenberg's endorsement of a bill put forward by a Democratic administration ensured that it would not be a party issue. Nonetheless, a number of Republicans opposed it. Taft in particular had a following. The son of a president and grandson of a cabinet secretary, the senior senator from Ohio represented bedrock Republicanism, fiscally conservative, pro-business, isolationist. In the Senate Vandenberg was supposed to lead for the Republicans in foreign affairs and Taft in domestic affairs, but Taft played a part in the Marshall Plan debate. Like many Republicans he was impressed by the anti-Communist argument but worried about other aspects of the program: it meant higher taxes, it smacked of welfare schemes, it financed socialist governments. He compared it to Roosevelt's New Deal, the Republicans' *bête noire*. He wanted to cut down the amount of aid on offer and to limit America's commitment to one year.

Others in the Senate, and in the House also, followed suit. Some pointed to the vast sums that America had given to Europe already, through Lend–Lease during the war, UNRRA and emergency aid, and asked why this program could be expected to achieve results that the others had not. In the House, forty-seven amendments were proposed, most of them designed to dilute the aid. Most were defeated. Some farm-state Republicans and Southern Democrats wanted to exclude grain, fertilizers, and farm machinery, which were in short supply in America, but these were just what was needed most and the move to exclude them was voted down.

No matter how many times Marshall and others pointed to American self-interest, some congressmen continued to characterize the plan as a give-away, Uncle Sam being seen as a soft touch. One thing they stressed often was that they wanted to be sure that at the end of the four-year program Europe would be able to stand on its own feet, that America would not be asked again to send aid.

Both houses of Congress finally passed the bill but added a preamble urging the recipient countries to join together to form a United States of Europe. As Charles Kindleberger said later, "The State Department held back from adding a political gloss ... Congress lacked such delicate inhibition, and it was this preamble that conveyed the emerging American policy of support for European economic integration." The bill became law on April 3, 1948. Within days a freighter sailed out of Galveston, Texas with the first shipment of Marshall aid, 9,000 tons of wheat. Soon there were fifty ships at sea carrying Marshall aid to Europe.

Congress had exacted its price. In the way that democracy American-style works, deals were struck and special interests had to be catered for to get the bill passed. Fifty percent of Marshall aid was to be carried in American ships. The Europeans had not asked for tobacco but they were going to get it, 40,000 tons over the next four years, guaranteeing the bill's support by congressmen from tobacco-growing states. At least a quarter of the wheat shipped had to be in the form of flour already processed in the United States. The export of scrap iron to Europe was limited to allow the export of finished iron and steel goods from America, to the profit of American manufacturers. To satisfy other American interests some 10,000 tons of American-made pasta were shipped to Europe, including to Italy, where the recipients no doubt made comparisons.

The plan was to extend over four years, but congressional committees were going to vote on each year's funds separately. Acheson commented on this in his memoirs: "Depending on the end of Pennsylvania Avenue from which one views the procedure, it is either insurance against executive extravagance or congressional usurpation and harassment. As might be expected, I strongly held the latter view, especially about the annual authorization, which seems to me the product of committee jealousy at its most picayune." This provision meant that the Administration might have to fight the battle for Marshall aid again every year. Taft gave a warning of this in the debate. "If I voted for this bill," he said, "it will be with the distinct understanding that we are making a one-year commitment. If we don't want to continue the program after the first year there is no commitment, moral, legal or otherwise, requiring that it be continued."

Throughout the debate the bill was presented as an anti-Communist measure. The Administration thought this was necessary. Dean Acheson wrote later that the American people would not have been moved to so great an effort simply to combat hunger in Europe. "I have probably made as many speeches and answered as many questions about the Marshall Plan as any man alive, except possibly Paul Hoffman," he said, "and what citizens and the representative in Congress alike always wanted to learn in the last analysis was how Marshall aid operated to block the extension of Soviet power."

The bill stipulated that a separate treaty had to be signed with every recipient country. With most this was a mere formality, but the British, as they did with the 1946 loan, persisted in looking this gift horse in the mouth. At a cabinet meeting ministers worried that it would allow the United States to interfere in British domestic policy, particularly on balancing the budget and purchases abroad. They were concerned also about the annual discussions in Congress about appropriations, which might expose British policies to scrutiny. The author of a cabinet paper said that the fact that the United States "has chosen to impose terms on the United Kingdom identical with those offered to Italy, an ex-enemy country, would gravely damage Anglo-American relations." But the same paper said that rejection of Marshall aid would be too grave a step to take.

There were critics in Parliament as well, reflecting, as did the cabinet debate, both pride and caution. Sir Stafford Cripps assured the House of Commons that Marshall aid would not commit the Government to any specific measures, but others were worried. Oliver Lyttelton said, "I shall vote for this measure but I shall vote for it reluctantly, and with some sense of humiliation." A handful of Labour MPs voted against it, and of course the two Communists, and a few right-wing Conservatives, did so too.

The opposition of the few Conservatives reflected a strain of anti-Americanism on the right that emerged occasionally in angry outbursts in the years after the war, at the time of the Suez episode and over Britain's colonies in Africa and, later in the Kennedy and Macmillan years, in the argument over the Skybolt missile. It was less ideological and more emotional than the anti-Soviet feeling. Communism was the enemy but it was the United States and not Russia that was replacing Britain as a global power, and was therefore an object of suspicion and resentment on the part of those most attached to this status. One of the last representatives of this view was Enoch Powell, a nationalist and imperialist whose tribal feeling about his country turned naturally to racism. This anti-American strain faded from Conservative politics with the passing of the generation that grew up with the empire.

In the spring of 1948 Italy was in the throes of an election campaign. In the last elections in 1946, the Communists had come in third place behind Prime Minister Alcide De Gasperi's Christian Democrats and the socialists, but now they had formed a coalition with the socialists, the People's Front. In municipal elections the People's Front had taken first place and seemed a possible winner in the national elections. People were angry and with poverty and hardship widespread they had a lot to be angry about. Even the Pope expressed pessimism about the outcome in a conversation with the US ambassador.

The prospect caused alarm in Washington. The American Embassy in Rome said in a dispatch, referring to a possible Communist victory: "So unprecedented an event must have a profound psychological effect in the countries threatened by the Soviets ... Militarily, the availability to the USSR of bases in Sicily and South Italy would pose a direct threat to the security of communications through the Mediterranean."

The rules of international conduct require that a country does not interfere in another country's elections, or at least that any interference is kept decently out of sight. The United States flouted this rule in the 1948 Italian elections. The American ambassador did not exactly stand on Christian Democrat platforms, but short of that the United States did everything to make its wishes known.

Shipments of Marshall aid food were coming in and the Americans made sure that every arrival was hailed by the Italian press, most of which was anti-Communist and happy to cooperate. The newly established Voice of America stepped up its broadcasts to Italy, with one after another group of Italian-Americans extolling the American way of life. Hollywood joined in, with an hour-long program in which Bing Crosby, Walter Pidgeon, and other film stars each spoke a few words of Italian, urging Italians not to let the country become a Communist dictatorship. This was broadcast over RAI, the national radio network. RAI trimmed some of the more self-congratulatory parts, where Americans told the world what a great country they lived in, which they thought would irritate listeners rather than impress them.

The State Department enlisted the help of Italian-American community organizations. These urged Italian-Americans to write to their relatives and friends in Italy warning them of the horrors of Communism. Sample post-cards and letters were sent out to help them. The five Italian-language newspapers in America (two in Philadelphia, one each in New York, Boston, and San Francisco), told their readers to cut out articles about the American way of life and the Communist threat and send them to relatives in Italy, at the suggestion of the State Department. They were also advised to tell them that if the Communists won, they would not be able to send any more gifts to Italy. Attorney-General Tom Clarke declared, "Those who do not believe in the American way of life should not be allowed to stay in the United States."

This was taken in Italy to mean that Italians who voted Communist would not be allowed to go to America.

America in secret funded parties, the Christian Democrats and, in particular, the breakaway socialists, who refused to ally themselves with the Communists and called themselves the Social Democratic Party. In this as in so many other things at this time, America was going where Britain had gone before. During World War One the British secret service had funded a socialist newspaper edited by Benito Mussolini which supported Italian entry into the war on the Allied side. In 1948 some of this American funding was handled by the Office of Policy Coordination, the OPC, an office in the State Department that took up some of the secret activities of the wartime Office of Strategic Services, as well as some of the personnel. Some of the money came from private donations, channelled through the law firm headed by Allen Dulles, who ran many OSS operations from Switzerland during the war and was now a private citizen with many connections in Washington. The American authorities knew that Russia was secretly funding the Communist Party.

In Italy, the Archbishops of Milan and Palermo said that anyone who voted Communist would not be given absolution. The Christian Democrats warned that if the Communists won, Italians would be sent to Russia as forced labor and children would become the property of the state.

The British Labour Party had links with the Italian socialists and reproached them for uniting with the Communists. "We sent condolences to Prague at the time of the coup, you sent congratulations," they said. When they failed to persuade them to break with the Communists, they threw their support behind the Social Democrat Party. A small group of left-wing Labour members of Parliament sent a telegram of good wishes to the other socialists, earning a rebuke from the party leadership.

Although the Communists were still presenting themselves as a legal and conventional political party, the United States was taking precautions against a Communist coup. An intelligence report from Rome said the Communists could probably win in a civil war but they would rather not provoke one. Nonetheless, when the Embassy pointed out that the Italian security forces needed weapons, the US Army turned a stockpile over to them, without going through the formalities of authorization from Congress. American warships called in at Genoa.

The anti-Communist campaigning had the desired effect. De Gasperi and the Christian Democrats won comfortably, with 48 percent of the vote, and the People's Front got 31 percent. For the first time in its history the United

States had thrown its weight on to one side in a European domestic political debate, and it had won.

In the same month that Czechoslovakia became a Communist country, President Truman signed the National Security Bill. This joined the service departments together in the Department of Defense, the Pentagon, and created the Central Intelligence Agency. In this new world that was developing, these were to be the two principal instruments for waging the Cold War. The CIA did not have many of the powers or the functions that it was to acquire later. It was an agency to gather and coordinate intelligence, with limited authority to engage in espionage. Truman was uncomfortable with the CIA and happy with the limitations. He worried that it could become a secret police force, a "gestapo," as he sometimes said.

The Marshall Plan divided Europe. When a ship docked with badly needed Marshall aid, it was welcomed with gratitude and sometimes a small ceremony while the Stars and Stripes flew alongside the national flag at the dockside. At Naples or Livorno or Marseilles, it might be met also by angry shouts and a picket line of demonstrators from one of the Communist-led unions trying to prevent dock workers unloading the ship.

Andrei Zhadanov, a top Soviet Politburo member and point man for the attacks on the plan, denounced it as part of "the American design to enslave Europe," and accused the West of seeking to "unleash a new war." He said the world was now divided into two camps, one standing for imperialism and anti-democratic forces, the other for peace and socialism.

The Soviet Union brought the Communist parties of eastern and western Europe together to create the Cominform, the Communist Information Bureau. This seemed to be a successor to the Comintern, or Third International, created in the wake of the Russian Revolution and dedicated to spreading Communism. It was disbanded in 1943 as a gesture of goodwill to Russia's Western allies. Zhadanov told the inaugural meeting of the Cominform that the Soviet Union would do all it could to ensure that the Marshall Plan failed. He said that Communist parties in western Europe should join this struggle, and "take up the standard in defense of the independence and sovereignty of their countries."

The United States, wielding a stiletto rather than a bludgeon, made a scar on Russia's image by publishing documents found at the end of the war in the German Foreign Ministry archives about the 1939 Nazi–Soviet pact. These did not provide any significant new information but they reminded the world of the Soviet Union's role at the outbreak of war.

The Marshall Plan created divisions within countries as well as between them. Communists in the West responded to Zhadanov's call to fight the plan. In France and Italy, where only a few months earlier they had been members of their governments and had rejected the label of revolutionaries, they redoubled their disruptive efforts, attacking Marshall aid and trying to prevent it landing.

The main French trade union group, the Confédération Général du Travail, CGT, was led by Communists and it followed the strict Communist line and fought the Marshall Plan. Communists dominated the meetings of the World Confederation of Free Trade Unions, the WFTU. Now a rival group was formed with secret British and American backing, the Confederation of Free Trade Unions, the CFTU. The Force Ouvrière in France and the main British and American trade unions joined it.

In Britain the division came on the left of the Labour Party. The Keep Left group, representing the left wing of the party, tended to be anti-American and wanted the Government to distance itself from American policies, but it could not bring itself to oppose Marshall aid. Only a handful of left-wingers spoke out against it and these now identified themselves as the pro-Communist fringe of the party.

In America the issue split off the left wing of the Democratic Party. The Americans for Democratic Action, representing the party's liberal wing, supported the Marshall Plan. But its most prominent figure, Henry Wallace, who had left the cabinet because he insisted that only Western policies stood in the way of friendship with Russia, criticized it. He said he was in favor of aid to Europe but the Marshall Plan was "in the spirit of the Truman Doctrine ... an instrument of cold war against Russia." With this view there was no place for him in the Democratic Party and he left to start his own party, the Progressive Party.

Today we see Communists as enemies of democracy but in the 1940s it did not always seem that way. Many people who believed in freedom and democracy were sympathetic to Communism. At this comfortable distance, when the battle between Communism and Western-style democracy is over, we can accept that most Communists, at least those in opposition, did not have villainous intent. Communism attracted some of the most intelligent and socially conscious among the working class, and many decent people of all classes. For these, being a Communist meant supporting the poor against the rich, the workers against the bosses. Marxism provided a philosophical framework for this. A Communist was likely to be the leader of a tenants' organization, a teacher working in a deprived area, or a doctor giving his services free to the poor. Communism, unlike, say, fascism or religious fundamentalism, shared the values of liberal democracy. Its adherents fought racism, not because they were using the issue to gain support, as some of their opponents said, but because they hated racism. Communists were on the left and many others on the left still looked on them as allies who differed on tactics. Even if they were not allies they were still on the same side of the barricades, and if one could not be with them, it went against the grain to support their reactionary opponents.

The Soviet Government did not behave democratically, but mitigating circumstances could be found. Russia was in a permanent state of war; the capitalist countries had sent in British and American troops to crush the revolution at its birth, and had been sending in spies and saboteurs since then. Marx had forecast the revolution coming first in advanced industrial countries, but it had come in a backward agrarian one, so it could not follow the expected path. Besides, American and British leaders who criticized the lack of freedom in eastern Europe had said nothing when those countries were under fascist regimes. And there were different kinds of democracy: democracy at the work place could be more meaningful than a choice at the ballot box once every few years.

Democratic socialists had to wonder sometimes whether they were fooling themselves in thinking they could change the system that was keeping down the working class by peaceful parliamentary means, and whether Communists, with their disciplined party and fewer scruples, were really fighting the battle that had to be fought. One quip on the left was "Communists are socialists who really mean it."

Here, in Lionel Trilling's novel *The Middle of the Journey*, about a group of American academics, is Laskell's relationship with his friend Maxim, who is a Communist: "It was understood between them that Laskell did not accept all of Maxim's ideas. At the same time Laskell did not oppose Maxim's ideas. One could not oppose them without being illiberal, even reactionary ... He was left very much exposed, not to Maxim's arguments, for Maxim seldom argued, but to his inner authority."

The cause gained respect from the sacrifices that people made for it. People gave money to the party who had little to spare. Men and women who worked hard all day put in more hours in party work. People gave their lives for its promise of a better world. Lola Ribar, a young Communist partisan in Nazi-occupied Yugoslavia, whose father was to become Vice-President, wrote a letter to be given to his fiancée in the event of his death, shortly before he was killed, "Do not mourn for me, dearest. In the world you will be living in, you will always find the best part of me." It was difficult to break faith with people like this and their aspirations.

The writer Ignazio Silone, who was a leading figure in the Italian

Communist Party when it operated underground under Mussolini's fascism and its members risked imprisonment and death, wrote of those days: "The links which bound us to the party grew steadily firmer, not in spite of the dangers and sacrifices involved, but because of them." For a Communist to abandon his convictions meant abandoning the belief in the better, fairer world that was to be brought into being. He faced the frightening prospect that confronts a religious believer whose faith is being eroded by doubts, of entering a bleak world without the purpose and the hope that had sustained him.

The struggle between Communism and democracy can be seen as a drama in which freedom in Europe was at stake. But because there were people on both sides impelled by decent instincts, it can also be seen as a tragedy.

Britain pulled out of two territories in the years after the war, leaving bloodshed behind. In 1947 the Attlee Government gave independence to India, the "jewel in the crown" of the British Empire, almost a year ahead of schedule, along with Burma and Ceylon (now Sri Lanka). Britain had hoped to leave a united India but the Muslim political leaders insisted on a separate Muslim entity, so India was divided into two countries, predominately Hindu India and Muslim Pakistan (the eastern part of Pakistan later became Bangladesh). The division was accompanied by widespread fighting between Hindus and Muslims. Hundreds of thousands were killed and tens of millions of people fled from their homes. In human suffering it was the most terrible event of the postwar years. But it made only a limited impact on Europe and America.

Palestine was also divided between two communities but the violence there had more impact on the West. The war between the Irgun, the Jewish terrorist underground group, and the occupying British forces intensified, with more killings and more repression. British warships stopped a ship loaded with illegal immigrants from Europe, the *Exodus*, after a skirmish in which two of the passengers and a crewman were killed. Usually, such would-be immigrants were taken to an internment camp in Cyprus, but the British transferred them to naval transports and took them back to Marseilles, their port of departure. The French refused to accept the Jews back so the British sent them on to the only part of the continent under their control, the British occupation zone of Germany. Newsreels all around the world showed British soldiers dragging people who had survived concentration camps off the ships at Hamburg, drawing worldwide condemnation. Returning Holocaust survivors to the land of their tormentors made Britain seem almost complicit in their suffering.

The American screenwriter and playwright Ben Hecht stoked up the emotional temperature, which was already high. He signed a full-page advertisement in American newspapers addressed to the Irgun that said, "Every time you blow up a British arsenal, or wreck a British jail, or send a British railroad sky-high, or let go with your guns and bombs at the British betrayers and invaders of your homeland, the Jews of America make a little holiday in their hearts." Those words "holiday in their hearts" became notorious in Britain. Many accepted his claim to speak for the Jews of America, and the Independent Theatre Owners, the cinemas association, banned films scripted by Hecht.

Fighting between Jews and Arabs in Palestine spread, a British effort to broker an agreement failed, and the British Government decided that it had had enough. It said it would leave Palestine in May 1948 and hand it over to the United Nations. The United Nations drew up a plan to partition the country between Jews and Arabs with a special status for Jerusalem. The Jews accepted it, the Arabs rejected it. An alternative suggestion was in the air – continued UN trusteeship. When this was being considered in Washington the Chiefs of Staff pointed out that this would require a large UN force to implement it to which the United States would be expected to contribute 40,000 troops, which it could not spare. In any case, dispatching American troops to Palestine would have been unacceptable to the public and President Truman promised that none would be sent. The left in America and elsewhere continued to support a Jewish state, a democratic homeland for the people who had suffered so much.

The struggle was reaching a climax. The Zionist dream of a country for the Jews, where they could not be persecuted and from which they could not be expelled, was in sight. Passions ran high. In America Jewish groups bombarded the Administration with their demands so insistently that it angered some members and risked being counter-productive, and stung Truman into making in private some uncharacteristically anti-Jewish remarks. Others were worried about relations with the Arab world. Forrestal told Truman that support for the Jewish state could alienate the whole Arab world. "Forty million Arabs are going to push 400,000 Jews into the sea. Oil – that is the side we ought to be on," he said.

Britain was seen to favor the Arabs on the ground. It was still turning away would-be immigrants. The Egyptian Army and Air Force had British arms and the Transjordan Army was commanded by a British general (Transjordan changed its name to Jordan later when it acquired territory across the Jordan river and occupied both banks). Things did not look good for the Jews in Palestine, who numbered only 650,000 and had only light weapons.

The fighting within the US Administration was almost as intense, if not as deadly, as the fighting in Palestine. The divide was between Truman and his advisors driven by domestic political considerations in an election year and the State Department driven by concern about relations with the Arab world. On the eve of Jewish statehood, Truman told Marshall that he intended to recognize the new state as soon as it came into being, which was what Clark Clifford was advising him to do. Marshall thought Truman was giving in to domestic pressure at the expense of the national interest and he argued against this, displaying an anger that no one had ever heard him show in the presence of his President. At one point, red-faced with emotion, he said to Truman, "If you follow Clifford's advice, and in the next election if I were to vote, I would not vote for you!"

Late in the afternoon of May 14, 1948 the last British High Commissioner for Palestine boarded a British cruiser to sail out of Haifa harbor as fighting spread across the country. In a small art museum in Tel Aviv, David Ben-Gurion, before a group of men and women, some of whom were in tears, raised his leonine head from his script and announced in a ringing voice the re-establishment of a Jewish state in the land of Palestine "by virtue of our natural and historic right and on the strength of the resolution of the United Nations General Assembly." It was to be called Israel, he said. He offered peace to Israel's Arab neighbors, but the offer was not accepted. At dawn the following morning the armies of Egypt, Transjordan, and Syria attacked and the new nation found itself fighting for its life. The United States officially recognized Israel and the Soviet Union followed suit.

Anglo-American differences over Israel have surfaced from time to time in the years since then. So have differences between the State Department and the White House, between international and domestic political considerations. In recent years domestic political considerations have won, and no alternative to support for Israel is voiced in Washington.

CHAPTER SIX

AMERICA TO THE RESCUE

Three years after the end of the war in Europe, when America thought it could turn its back on the old continent, Americans were back in Europe with Marshall aid. It was not American soldiers this time, but diplomats, industrialists, businessmen-as-diplomats, businessmen-as-advisors, academics, lawyers, trade unionists, interfering in and occasionally directing the affairs of European countries on many levels. As F. Taylor Ostrander, a Marshall Plan official in Germany and Austria, wrote later, "There may never have been a time, before or since, when the United States was so intimately engaged in helping Europeans in all walks of life, or when such American help was so willingly, even eagerly, accepted by Europeans."

Congress had decreed that the administration of Marshall aid should be independent of the State Department, so in the spring of 1948 the Government set up a new agency, the Economic Cooperation Administration, the ECA. It was to have a life of four years, the duration of the Marshall Plan. Truman wanted to appoint Acheson director of the ECA and Marshall wanted Clayton. But Vandenberg, reflecting Congress's suspicion of the State Department, insisted that someone from the world of business should head it.

Truman canvassed opinion from leading businessmen and the name most often mentioned was Paul G. Hoffman. Hoffman had risen from being a car salesman to the presidency of the Studebaker automobile company, and had played a part during the war in organizing industry for the war effort. He regarded himself as a responsible capitalist; under his stewardship, labor relations at Studebaker were a model for the industry, and he had devised urban traffic schemes for the city of Los Angeles. It was also in his favor that he was a Republican. Truman offered him the job, but Hoffman said he did not want it, and he stuck to this despite Truman's urgings. So Truman simply announced to the press that he had been appointed, and Hoffman felt he could not repudiate the President.

Once Hoffman took the job he promoted the Marshall Plan with evangelical fervor, addressing audiences across America, and he became a public figure. The following year *Collier's* magazine included him in its list of "The

25 Men Who Rule the World." Hoffman had faith in American-style free enterprise and believed it would defeat Communism by example. "The battle is between the Communist Party line and the American assembly line," he said once.

He worked from the Statler Hotel in Washington for the first two months before he took offices for his new agency in the Mariatico building. Two days after the ERP bill was passed he telephoned Richard Bissell, who taught economics at MIT. Bissell had acquired a good reputation in Washington during the war as head of the War Shipping Administration. He was also one of the authors of the Harriman committee report on aid to Europe, which he wrote along with two other old friends from Yale, Max Milliken and Fritz Liebert. Hoffman told him he needed him right away. Bissell pointed out that he had classes to teach and could not come until the weekend, but Hoffman insisted that he had to set off immediately. When Bissell said he could not get a hotel room at such short notice, Hoffman replied that they could put an extra bed in his room at the Statler. So Bissell took the train to Washington and arrived at midnight. Hoffman told him there would be a meeting of most of the ECA staff the following morning at seven o'clock in his hotel room. The staff consisted of ten people.

The day after that Nitze came over from the State Department with fifty or sixty procurement documents that he said were urgent and Bissell signed authorizations for $35 million. Bissell moved his family down from Cambridge. His students would have to make do with another teacher for the rest of the term.

Bissell was the tactician of the ECA, setting out European demands in order of priority, matching aid to each country's needs as he saw them. With a sharp mind and a Groton–Yale background he fitted in well with the influential Georgetown circle of senior officials, diplomats, and a few journalists. Six months after he joined the ECA, a report from the British Embassy to the Foreign Office said, "Richard Bissell, a New Dealish college professor, is emerging as the most influential member."

Hoffman hired other people, from the financial world, industry, academia, and government, many of them on short-term contracts. For most, certainly those coming from finance or industry, it involved a drop in salary. Some joined the ECA because they felt it their duty to help the Government, some because it was a new challenge, some because it meant being part of a great adventure, most for all three reasons.

To manage the ERP in Europe Truman chose Averell Harriman, his Secretary of Commerce. Harriman was a veteran of international diplomacy, former ambassador to Moscow and an establishment in-and-outer. His title was US Special Representative and he had the rank of ambassador. For his offices the American Government rented one of the grandest mansions in Paris, the splendidly furnished eighteenth-century Hôtel Talleyrand on the vast Place de la Concorde, the plaza at the center of Paris, close to the American Embassy (the French word *hôtel* can also mean mansion or town house). Harriman put a bust of Benjamin Franklin, the first American minister in Paris, in his office. In its salons he had carpenters build what one reporter called "a labyrinthine maze of cubicles, pens and partitions" to accommodate his burgeoning staff, and downstairs a snack bar selling hot dogs and American ice cream. Today the building houses the consular offices of the US Embassy.

Despite his diplomatic experience, Harriman sometimes generated friction with the Europeans he dealt with, and among some Americans too. Kennan, who had served under him at the Moscow Embassy, liked him but said he did not know why. Some found Harriman's manner imperious. A British Foreign Office memo said, "The ECA cannot understand why people were not prepared to travel to Paris to have the privilege of meeting Mr Harriman."

Most members of the Committee on European Economic Cooperation assumed that now that it had presented its findings it would be disbanded. But the ECA insisted that it remain in existence and continue to be the principal receiving agency for Marshall aid, so it turned itself into the Organization for European Economic Cooperation, the OEEC. This became a permanent body. In 1987 it added industrial countries outside Europe to its membership and became the Organization for Economic Cooperation and Development, the OECD.

The American demand that Europe stand on its own feet took effect right away. Harriman told the OEEC members that it was up to them to parcel out among themselves the first year's package of aid. They were aghast at the prospect of getting agreement on a fair division. After some arguing the OEEC council appointed a group of four civil servants from Britain, France, Italy, and the Netherlands to divide up the aid. The four withdrew to Chantilly, twenty-five miles away, to work out their plan, and received representatives of the sixteen countries one at a time to present their claims.

When they brought their plan back to the full sixteen-member council, as one member said, "pandemonium broke loose." Everyone thought that in some way they were not getting their fair share. Battered by protests from all sides the French member of the group of four, Georges Guidney, pleaded,

"We've done our best. We have tried to apply the same rules to each country. I don't think we can make any other reply." It took weeks to work out an agreed version of the plan to present to the ECA.

In these arguments and others over intra-European payments, West Germany, which had no government and therefore no delegate, turned out paradoxically to have an advantage. Its interests were represented by the Western occupying powers. The American representative, Lawrence Wilkinson, as keen as the US occupation commander General Clay to push German interests, pulled rank on the others as an American. He warned them that if they reduced the amount he was asking for Germany this would make a bad impression on Congress and it might cut their appropriations for the second year.

The ECA established offices in every European country that received Marshall aid, each office headed by an American, usually from the world of business, and each with a sizeable staff, swelling the American presence. From America Europe seemed like an exciting place and among many of those who had worked on aid in Washington there was a rush to get a job there. Europe was the new frontier. Hubert F. Havlik, who worked in the Treasury, recalled,

> Many of us had been cooped up in Washington day and night with short or no vacations for a period of two years working on all these programs I have mentioned. And now the Marshall plan was really getting moving, establishing missions in all of the Marshall plan countries, the action would be there. This was a chance to go to Denmark, to England, or to Italy, and so on. And what happened? Lo and behold, it was just like opening the door of a chicken coop; suddenly you open the door, and the chickens fly out.

The London office had fifty-five staff members, most with families, plus fourteen British clerks and chauffeurs. The head of the mission was Thomas K. Finletter, a lawyer and member of the US delegation to the founding meeting of the United Nations. He was on the liberal wing of the Democratic Party and unlike most American officials he was sympathetic to the Labour Government and its policies, so much so that, as Richard Bissell recalled, "We were suspicious that the mission reflected the view of the British Government." Finletter was also a signatory of the 1946 declaration advocating world federalism along with Cord Meyer. He served in London until June 1949, when he went back to Washington to become Air Force Secretary. Until there was something like world government, he wanted America to be strong.

The Paris representative was David Bruce, a Virginia gentleman who had been in Paris with the OSS during the war. Wealthy, cosmopolitan, French speaking, he dealt ably and sympathetically with the French Government and he and his wife Evangeline entered and enhanced the capital's *haute monde*.

The ECA headquarters spread beyond its offices on the Place de Concorde. Its several divisions, Industry, Trade and Payments, Labor, and others, acquired offices in buildings nearby. At one point, ECA staff and their families in Paris amounted to 7,500 people. They had their own snack bars and their own community support systems. Driving their big American cars, addressing waiters and bartenders loudly in English, they made their presence felt and sometimes resented. Janet Flanner wrote in the *New Yorker*, "The French are tired of being occupied."

In addition to the expanding number of officials, more Americans were going to Europe on their own. The dollar was strong, and living anywhere in Europe was inexpensive. Paris in particular still had some of the attractions of its prewar status as a center of literary life, a home from home for American bohemia. Elliot Paul's elegiac account of his years in Paris between the wars, *The Last Time I Saw Paris* (published in Britain as *A Narrow Street*) was a bestseller during the war when Paris could not be visited. Now the dark night of German occupation was over and these young Americans could stroll along the cobbled streets and talk about literature over *fines* in Left Bank cafés, in the footsteps of Hemingway and Fitzgerald. Americans went to study in Europe with grants under the GI Bill, or, if not to study, at least to hang around the student cafés.

Americans in Europe then were like Westerners in the Third World today, coming from a more prosperous society, accustomed to comforts unavailable to all but the wealthiest of the natives, and relying for some of what they regarded as the necessities of life on either the US Embassy commissariat, an Army PX store or packages from home. Whether they were living on a salary or a student grant or checks from indulgent parents, they were usually better off than most people in their host country.

ECA Americans had come over to remake Europe, to put it together again with good old American know-how. With goodwill, enthusiasm, and cultural insensitivity, men newly arrived from campus or industry or farm organization were deciding what to do about German coal mines, French canals, Danish farmland. Americans are natural problem-solvers. Europe was a problem to be solved.

The American journalist Theodore White gives a vivid picture of after-work conversations at the Crillon bar on the Place de la Concorde, next door to the Hôtel Talleyrand:

> They say they want to know how much wheat France is going to be able to export, so they ask how many tractors will France need to raise that much wheat ... Well, we get to work and we produce a figure and we give it to the commercial boys and they say how many of these do you think France can make herself, then somebody else says so many and somebody else says when?... Turkey, that's really fouled up. I figure they could raise maybe a million tons of wheat there, but somebody else says there's no water. So we figure we could irrigate the land, and somebody else says how are you going to move that million tons of wheat out of there? By mule cart? Then after you get through figuring out how to put in the machinery, the irrigation and the railways, you find out they've got 800,000 wooden ploughs there and if the wheat market goes down it'll squeeze the peasants out and they're liable to blow up the machinery and the railways. Every time you touch something it gets tangled up in something else. *Garcon*, two more drys.

The ECA mission heads were almost like proconsuls, giving advice that was impossible to ignore and difficult to contradict. Few of them spoke the language of the country to which they were assigned, so government officials who wanted to talk to them directly had to learn English. Where they and Europeans worked together on committees, the situation resembled the old British Empire formula of native troops led by white officers.

In the first year of the ERP, half the aid was food. After that aid came in many different forms. The ECA introduced rice production into Greece. It persuaded the Greek Government that it needed a road system after the local ECA chief, Paul Porter, noticed that although there was a fishing industry you could not get fish ten miles inland. It began the mechanization of French agriculture, so that in 1950 France had four times as many tractors as in 1940. Germany created the Institute for Credit for Reconstruction, the *KfW Bankengruppe*, to disburse Marshall aid funds, and it plays a part in German economic life today.

Sometimes the impact of Marshall aid was immediate. Europe's biggest tyre plant, in Birmingham, England, was idle because it could not get carbon black, a vital ingredient, and its 10,000 workers faced losing their jobs. Normally this was purchased from America, but the Government would not allow the plant to buy it since the country could not afford the outflow of dollars. Carbon black came with Marshall aid and the plant was soon operating at capacity. The British Government's official Economic Survey for 1949 said, "There is not a single industry or district in the country that has not benefited in some way from American aid."

Even the weather favored the Marshall Plan in that first year. Having experienced in the previous year a destructive winter and a scorching dry summer that shriveled crops, Europe was now treated to a warm summer with plentiful rain, which produced bumper harvests. It made it a great time to sit at outdoor cafés, and brought out the best in the chestnut trees along the Champs Elysées and in the willows in St James's Park.

In southern Germany ECA officials encouraged the creation of collective farms and supplied agricultural equipment for them. The local press dubbed these "white collectives," in contrast to the "red collectives" that were being established in the Soviet zone. Hybrid maize from the American south was transplanted in the Pyrenees. Elastic steel-refining was developed in Norway, synthetic yarn in British textile mills. Inspired by the Tennessee Valley Authority, hydroelectric dams were built in Languedoc in France and in Sardinia.

Sometimes the ECA's interference in the lives of Europeans was breathtaking. Italy had two million unemployed and its population was increasing. The ECA in Rome decided that Italy did not have enough jobs for its people and the answer was emigration to South America. Without telling the Italian Government, it brought in Rockefeller Foundation expertise to advise on the economic and social ramifications of this. Then it worked with the Government to encourage emigration, gave money to expand the Italian steamship line, and directed some money to Brazil to facilitate Italian migration to that country. Emigration went up, from 54,000 in 1947 to 150,000 in 1949. There are Brazilians today with Italian forebears who owe the fact that they were born in South America to a decision made by some Americans employed on a short-term contract by the ECA.

In addition to disbursing aid, the United States exerted influence over the finances of European governments through what were called "counterpart funds." When a country received material US aid, as opposed to money, it had to set aside an equivalent sum of money in the local currency, and this was called a counterpart fund. The ECA gave this example in explaining it. A French farmer, Albert Jolivet, with ninety acres in Plainpied, wanted a tractor. The American Government had sent tractors to France as Marshall aid. Jolivet bought one of these tractors and paid the French Government 500,000 francs. This was deposited in the counterpart fund. The French Government could spend 95 percent of this, but the ECA had a veto over its use. The other 5 percent would go to finance American activities in Europe.

In France some of this money went to finance the Monnet Plan for modernization – indeed it was essential to it. David Bruce gave the plan his full backing. Monnet wrote to Prime Minister Robert Schuman: "It has now become possible to achieve the Monnet Plan thanks to Marshall credits." In Britain the Treasury used counterpart funds to reduce the national debt.

The ECA sometimes exercised its veto. Austria wanted to use counterpart funds to rebuild the Vienna Opera House, and this was refused. It was also refused permission to invest counterpart funds with a textiles entrepreneur who ECA officials thought had a dodgy business record. The French Government wanted to use some to build a casino. This made economic sense; the casino would more than pay for itself with its earnings and by bringing in tourism. But ECA officials had a good idea what opponents of the Marshall Plan back home would make of American taxpayers' money going to build a casino for the lazy pleasure-loving French, and they vetoed the plan.

The ECA did not always get its way. It refused at first to allow the French Government counterpart funds to support a reduction in interest rates, which would have eased pressure on the economy. It thought this would merely shore up inefficient businesses. French ministers said that their Government, a coalition of parties like all French governments, would fall if the economy did not show a rapid improvement, and might be replaced by a more extreme government to the left or right. ECA officials yielded to the political argument. In Italy also, they sometimes had to give way on the economics to avoid weakening the Government.

William Tomlinson, a young US Treasury official seconded to the ECA, became notorious in the ECA for cracking the counterpart whip. At one point he addressed the French Government in schoolmasterish tones, saying that ministers would be allowed no further use of counterpart funds "until they were prepared to explain why their overall economic program had not maintained a satisfactory degree of fiscal and price stability and what they were prepared to do about it." However, like Bruce, he backed the Monnet Plan.

In Italy the bureaucratic process was sometimes cumbersome. In July 1948 a large engineering company in Reggio Emilia asked for eighty machine tools worth $1,240,000. The request was authorized in March the following year but there was a hold-up over credits and the machines arrived two years after the original request. By then it was too late and the company went into liquidation. Some of the Italians organizing the distribution of Marshall aid were former fascists. One had been at the Italian Embassy in Berlin and was such an enthusiast for Nazism that when Italy left the war he joined the SS.

The ECA favored free-market capitalism, but, in economics as in politics, it supported the non-Communist left. It urged governments to curb inflation which hit wage-earners. It supported low-cost housing. The Italian Government wanted a grant to repair and enlarge the Fiat car plant, damaged by wartime bombing. The ECA said it could have it provided Fiat produced small, low-cost cars for the lower-middle income groups. However, the ECA forced Italy to adopt a deflationary policy which kept down wages but made it easier to export and benefited the economy in the long run. One employee, a writer who made a documentary film about the Marshall Plan, left the ECA complaining that it was "a briar patch of liberalism," and joined the CIA. Howard Hunt would later come into the public eye as one of the Watergate burglars.

Most of the Marshall aid money remained in America, spent by the Government on American goods to be shipped to Europe. *Kiplinger* magazine, a business publication, carried a guide on how business could profit from the ERP, and commented, "The Marshall Plan is very much a business plan. At its root is an office and factory and warehouse job. The Marshall Plan means work and you will be one of the workers."

It was good for American business. It averted a recession due to overproduction, as the State Department had forecast. At one time Marshall aid was 5 percent of America's gross national product. It created a market for American investment. As an official publication stated, "Encouragement of private capital in Western Europe is in accordance with a principal end objective of the plan." In 1949 a congressional amendment to the second year's appropriations bill required the ECA to establish an Office of Small Business to help smaller firms in America get a piece of the ECA action.

There were clashes in Congress when it had to authorize the second year's spending. This gave a few congressmen another chance to take pot shots at Marshall aid. A few attacked Britain's socialist measures. Senator James P. Kemp of Missouri moved an amendment to bar aid to any country that nationalized its steel industry, which Britain was in the process of doing. Vandenberg as usual sprang to the ERP's defense. He insisted, "So long as Britain is a free and independent people making free and independent decisions regarding a type of economy under which they want to operate, I do not believe it is any of our business." Old-guard isolationists kept up their drum beat of opposition. In a typical editorial the *Chicago Tribune*, the voice of Midwestern conservatism, said, "As long as Mr. Truman begs, hat in hand, for the privilege of paying their deficits and fighting their battles, the European countries are under no compulsion to use their own considerable assets and talents in a co-operative effort to the same ends."

The House of Representatives voted for an amendment to include Spain in the program. Communists in Europe seized on this and made great play with it, while moderates were appalled. Bevin cabled Marshall: "It seems to make the whole Marshall Plan appear as a line-up behind fascism and reaction and is causing great anxiety among our best friends." On the strong advice of the State Department the Senate rejected the proposal.

If there was American self-interest in the Marshall Plan, some Europeans saw nothing else. A poll taken in France found that two-thirds of people believed the plan was motivated by America's need for foreign markets and its desire to interfere in European affairs. The percentage was slightly lower in Britain: about half thought America had selfish motives in the Marshall aid program, a proportion that rose to two-thirds among the working class. However, the Trades Union Congress welcomed it as a sign of "the generosity of the American people."

America wanted a message to go with the Marshall Plan, about America and the American way. The Voice of America had started broadcasting to Europe the previous year, not without a certain amount of opposition from congressmen who thought it was a waste of money. Congressman John Jennings from Tennessee said: "If the people all over Europe do not know that we are the kindest, most generous, most sympathetic people on the face of the earth, no amount of silly broadcasting will enable them to realize these facts." A *Washington Post* executive, Alfred Friendly, was made head of Marshall Plan publicity. Friendly and his team created radio programs, documentary films, magazine articles, and posters designed to reveal the benefits of Marshall aid and to show America in a good light. Often these employed European film-makers and broadcasters. A mobile Marshall Plan exhibition toured Europe with films and a puppet show in several languages.

There were disagreements between the ECA in Europe and in Washington about the nature of this publicity. The ECA in Washington wanted a high profile given to Marshall aid projects, which the missions in Europe thought might be counter-productive. Tomlinson dismissed their plans as "the bronze plaque approach, with red, white and blue fountains in public squares." Nonetheless, they made sure that when a factory was set up or modernized with Marshall aid money, the workers knew where the money came from.

Some of the publicity was subtle and indirect. As an internal ECA report noted: "American propaganda arouses a degree of suspicion, disbelief and animosity on the part of Europeans." So the aim should be to "get across the ECA and the US Government foreign policy point of view without the US Government or the ECA being identified as the source of the material." Articles were planted in European newspapers. *Answers*, a popular radio program that was distributed to radio stations in several languages, dealt with questions sent in by listeners on anything from astronomy to zoology. There was always one question about America - American workers, the constitution, race - that produced a positive answer. The ECA paid for subscriptions to leading American newspapers and magazines for libraries and schools all over Europe, drawing criticism from some newspapers not so favored.

This became part of a wider attempt to project the more positive aspects of the American way of life abroad. Were Afro-Americans oppressed? Articles by or about prominent Afro-Americans were distributed to European magazines. Was America a philistine, materialistic country? The US Government sponsored tours by the Boston Symphony Orchestra, and traveling exhibitions of modern American art.

If there was one area in which Americans were sure that they could teach Europeans a lot, it was efficiency. The gap in efficiency between America and any European country was vast. A team of British economists found that on average American industry was nearly 2.5 times as efficient as British industry. A General Motors car worker produced six times as much as a Renault worker, and he was paid seven times as much. Americans thought they had the answer. Paul Hoffman said European workers must learn that America was "the land of full shelves and bulging shops made possible by high productivity and good wages." European management could not help being impressed by the fact that American blue-collar workers had cars while European workers rode to work on bicycles and did not have refrigerators. Americans criticized European industry for its cartels and combines, its lack of competition, its resistance to change.

In Britain Sir Stafford Cripps, President of the Board of Trade, and Thomas Finletter set up the Anglo-American Productivity Council. The response surprised Cripps and showed how prickly British pride could be. In Parliament left-wing and trade union MPs said British workers did not need to learn from America and were not going to be taken over by American management methods. In Washington, when Hoffman gave a press conference about the scheme, a British correspondent asked him whether Americans were prepared to learn anything from British management. He replied tactfully that he would be happy to accept any advice.

Other productivity councils were set up. Groups of European industrialists, and trade unionists also, visited American factories to learn American ways. Dutch farmers studied grain farms in Iowa. Norwegian coal miners looked at mines, Italians investigated hybrid corn, Turks learned about road-building and civil aviation. Most visitors came back with new ideas. The Italian steel industry decided to introduce management training. The French were impressed by the more open and casual staff relations; they were surprised to learn that 45 percent of American firms told their workers about plans for changes or new designs before they told their customers. One French industrialist reported that American factories were clean, orderly, quiet, and well lit, while many in France were "dark, dingy factories with filthy floors and horrible noise ... more like prisons than places where men have to spend a third of their lives."

Reading reports by the British teams, one sees a number of themes emerge again and again which shed light on attitudes of the time. One is the fear of becoming Americanized. The report by the Management Accounting Team met this head-on. "The achievement of an equal degree of efficiency in no way requires the sacrifice of the best characteristics of the British way of life," it said. Several drew attention to the greater involvement of workers, and hence to the workers' stake in improved productivity. American businesses, if not always American unions, pointed to the common interest of workers and management in improved productivity and higher profits. This was the message the American Government wanted to get across: cooperation was the way, not class war and labor militancy. One labor group from Britain, evidently convinced by this message, came back and reported: "Unions should seek to co-operate in the application of 'scientific management' which, even if it is not an exact science, can make a valuable contribution to increasing productivity in industry." In those days in Britain the term "scientific management" was put in quotes.

Some delegations stressed the pull and push on the American worker, the pull being the desire to buy more, the push being the fear of losing his or her job. As the report of the Steel Founding Industry team said: "Incentives include not only the high standard of living and the pressure exerted on the wage earner by his womenfolk to raise his standard higher but also the compulsion of fear. In the absence of unemployment benefits comparable with British practice, the consequences of falling out of a job can be disastrous ... This has been described as part of the American way of life."

Mother's Day, then unknown in Britain, was cited as a marketing tool, part of the intensive marketing designed to get people to buy more and hence to want to earn more. One report quoted a British writer, Francis Williams, who made the point neatly that American workers and their bosses did not belong to different cultures, as they often seemed to in Britain: "American workers and American management do not like each other, but they like the same things."

During the Marshall Plan years, 138 groups comprising 900 people went to America from Britain alone. Despite the positive reports brought back, a working culture could not be changed quickly. In July 1949 a disappointed Sir Stafford Cripps reported to the cabinet that "comparatively little progress has been made towards levels of productivity comparable to North America." If unions were sometimes resistant to change, this was not without reason. A team of American union representatives that went to Europe reported that there was no mechanism to protect workers against unemployment caused by higher productivity.

Americans usually think that the answer to another people's problems is for them to become more like Americans. In Europe this meant running their industries and farms more efficiently, American-style. It also meant joining together as the American states once joined together, to create one market, and ideally one political unit which would stop these wars that had been plaguing the world. As the (London) *Times* correspondent in Washington reported:

> For some weeks the United States has been swept by the urge to transfer to old Europe the benefits of the Federal system. Like other countries it tends to think of foreign problems in terms of its own experience. For instance, many speeches in favor of the Marshall Plan have drawn a parallel with the failure of the North to reconstruct the South after the civil war. In the same way, the foresight of the men who framed the constitution has been quoted as an example to the statesmen of Western Europe.

The parallel of a possible federal Europe with the creation of America as a union of states is far from exact but it was pervasive. *Life* magazine said: "To more and more thinking people, our policy should be to help the nations of Europe federate as our states federated in 1787." The *St Louis Post-Dispatch* wrote: "Like the famous advice Benjamin Franklin gave to the American colonies, for Europe it is a case of join or die." This was an old idea. George Washington wrote to the Marquis de Lafayette: "We have sowed seeds of liberty and union that will spring up everywhere on earth, and one day, taking its pattern from the United States of America, there will be founded the United States of Europe."

Soon after General Marshall made his speech at Harvard, three senior State Department officials, Charles Kindleberger, Harold van Buren Cleveland, and Ben Moore, wrote a far-reaching memorandum on European integration. They said:

> The symbols of nationalism in France and Italy and in Germany are essentially bankrupt and in danger of being captured by reactionary and

> neo-fascist political elements which we do not wish to support. There is a possibility of developing tremendous emotional drive in Western Europe behind the supra-national idea of European unity ... To avoid injuring sensitive feelings of nationalism, our appeal should be couched in terms of a European recovery plan which stresses the raising of European production and consumption through the economic and "functional" unification of Europe.* In our propaganda and our diplomacy it will be necessary to stress (even exaggerate) the immediate economic benefits which will flow from the joint making of national economic policies and decisions.

They went on to give specific examples of inefficiencies brought on by the existence of economic frontiers: coal mines in Britain and France were short of labor while 2.5 million Italians were unemployed. German steel was being used to make toy trains and cameras for export to America rather than spare parts for European machinery. In Holland and in Greece vegetables were rotting for lack of transport while people suffered vitamin deficiency.

They were right about the poor standing of the symbols of nationalism. No government on the European continent had given its people much reason for national pride during the war years. Most countries shared the experience of defeat and Nazi occupation. It was difficult for a German in those years to feel, and still less to assert, pride in being German. But to be granted the status of European offered a chance of being accepted once again into the family of nations. It seemed to many that European unity was an idea whose time had come.

After the war a number of political figures out of office created a European Movement. It was given a boost, surprisingly, by that British patriot Winston Churchill, in a speech in Zurich in September 1946, a speech remembered on the continent more than it is in his own country. Churchill described the greatness of Europe and the desperate plight of many of its citizens at that time, and then turned to the remedy for their plight. "What is this sovereign remedy? It is to recreate the European family, or as much of it as we can, and to provide it with a structure under which it can dwell in peace, in safety and in freedom. We must build a United States of Europe." He was cheered to the rafters and his support was cited enthusiastically by European integrationists, yet in the speech he gave Britain a detached place in this European family. Britain, like the Commonwealth, America, and even Russia, he said, must be

* Prime Minister Edward Heath followed this approach when he took Britain into the European Common Market, presenting it as a purely functional measure for economic advantage and downplaying any wider implications.

"the friends and sponsors of the new Europe." He did not say it was to be a part of it.

Bevin was originally an enthusiast for greater European unity. The economic ministries in Whitehall were not, however. When a customs union was being considered, the British ambassador in Paris, Duff Cooper, wrote in his diary: "The question of a customs union is causing difficulty. It would please the Americans, the French are for it, and our ministers are willing, but the officials of the Treasury and the Board of Trade - pig-headed as ever - won't hear of it. We need only accept the principle. The thing itself will not come for years." The Treasury preferred to concentrate on the sterling area and worried about opening up Britain's borders completely to goods from the continent. The Labour Party also did not want integration with Europe. It had waited for years to put into practice its program of establishing a welfare state, nationalizing key industries, and establishing tight government control over the economy. It was not going to risk this by merging a large part of Britain's economy with that of other countries.

Integration with Europe was also contrary to the spirit of the British people at this time. Many on the continent may not have felt much pride in their country, but Britons did. British people felt keenly this difference between their country and those on the continent. Just as many pro-integrationists, while they talked of economic advantages, were propelled by deeper feelings about unity as Europeans, so many British people, while rejecting the idea on economic grounds, were reflecting deeper feelings that their history and culture were separate and different and perhaps - at least as reflected in recent behavior - superior. A BBC radio program in 2006 reported Attlee as saying, when Britain was invited to join with France, the Benelux countries, Italy, and Germany in the first moves towards integration: "I don't want to go crawling to a group of nations four of whom we have had to rescue from the other two." The language sounds too dramatic for Attlee, but somebody must have said it.

There were difficulties for others also. The Dutch were worried that France and Italy would dominate a European entity and said they would join only if Britain also joined as a counterbalance to France. Moreover, for a government to give up its right to impose import duties and establish tariffs is to give up some of the most important tools at its disposal for managing its economy, even if the larger market brings benefits in the long run.

The issue of integration arose with the establishment of the OEEC to handle Marshall Plan funds. The French and others, with American backing, wanted it to be a supranational body, taking decisions for Europe. They wanted it to have majority voting, a strong executive and a secretary-general with real powers of decision. But the British insisted that it should consist of national delegations representing their governments and responsible to them. Harriman complained that Britain had not given the OEEC the importance it should have had and had not appointed a sufficiently senior figure as its representative in the organisation. Bevin told Lewis Douglas, the US ambassador, that he resented being told whom he should appoint to a diplomatic post. "America would be well advised to let us do business in our own way," he said. But it was not about whom to appoint; the level of the appointment to the OEEC would indicate the importance and power given to it.

From the State Department, Marshall messaged Douglas in London: "Hoffman has expressed grave concern over British attitude and feels they are not entering wholeheartedly into OEEC work. He further believes that unless they exercise real leadership to initiate and push forward effective measures for economic co-operation among EEC members, there is good chance OEEC will fail." He went on to hint that he might bring serious pressure on Britain: "We consider that solution may well involve steps taken on our part affecting whole range of US–UK relations beyond those arising directly from ERP." The threat was never carried out but the pattern was set, and was to persist for the next two decades, European countries drawing closer, America encouraging, Britain resisting. As George Kennan wrote in a dispatch, "The United Kingdom has tended to exert a retarding influence on the Western European plans for closer political and economic integration."

Yet Britain could have been the natural leader of Europe. The Herter Committee's report said that, among the European countries, Britain alone possessed "the past experience and the present economic resources and political stability necessary for bold and imaginative leadership." Europeans would have welcomed British leadership. People on the continent admired Britain for its stand in the war and for its social and political stability. Frenchmen and Italians contrasted this with the situation in their own countries, with fistfights in parliaments, demonstrations that become riots, and fears of a coup from left or right. A member of the French National Assembly told a *New York Times* correspondent: "We French don't have the civic spirit of the British, and that makes governing difficult." Most people on the continent would have been happy to tie their countries to Britain in a European organization in order to gain from this stability, like an unstable craft in the water roped to a more stable one. Anyone who traveled in Europe in the years after the war can testify to the prestige which attached to Britain.

Here is one story to illustrate the point. In 1950 there was a strike in France of transport and communications workers. Hundreds of British holidaymakers were arriving by cross-Channel ferry in Calais to find themselves stranded in the port area, with no trains to take them on further. Some British journalists arrived to report on their plight. They wanted to telephone their stories back to their London offices. In those days all long-distance calls went through the operator. French operators manned the switchboards so that they could handle emergency calls to hospitals or the police but they refused resolutely to put through the reporters' calls. But when a BBC correspondent asked to be put through the operator said, "Oh yes. We remember the BBC from the war. We'd be glad to do something for the BBC."

Here is another, from the author's own experience. Although it took place some years after this period it relates to it. In 1965 my next-door neighbor in London was a pleasant Dutch woman, a lawyer. We talked about politics occasionally. She held strong leftwing convictions, very hostile to Conservatives, big business, and the royal family. I was working for an American radio news service, and one day I came home from reporting plans for Winston Churchill's funeral the following week and met her on the doorstep. She was looking haggard and I suggested she come in for a drink.

She accepted and collapsed into an armchair. "I'm exhausted. I waited in line for an hour in the rain," she told me. I asked her where she had been waiting. "To see Churchill lying in state," she explained.

I was amazed. "Why on earth did you want to see Churchill lying in state?" I asked. "The arch-Conservative? In a royal chapel?"

She in turn was amazed at my question. "But that was Churchill!" she said. "Do you know what Churchill meant to us during the war? Have you any *idea*?" And she told me, with tears of emotion, about hearing Churchill speaking on the radio in occupied Holland. There was a lot of static and she did not speak English well so she only understood a part of what he said. But she was thrilled at the thought that this was a voice from Britain, and Britain was still free and still fighting. Her friends asked her eagerly, "What did he say? What did he *sound* like?" "Of course I had to see Churchill lying in state," she insisted.

In May 1948, shortly after the OEEC was created, the European Movement, a body with no official standing but a lot of political support, organized a Congress of Europe in the Hague with 750 participants. Churchill, his Zurich speech remembered, was named honorary president. Many people who were playing or would play a part in European governments were present, including François Mitterrand, Konrad Adenauer, Belgium's Paul-Henri Spaak, and Léon Blum, the French Socialist and former premier. There were also a few intellectual stars to add luster, among them Bertrand Russell and Salvador de Madariaga.

The Congress decided to set up a European Assembly and a European Court of Human Rights. Once again the British were reluctant and raised objections. It is on this subject that Bevin is reported to have uttered his memorable jumble of metaphors: "If you open that Pandora's box you'll find it full of Trojan horses." The French invited Britain and the Benelux countries to study the proposal, assuring Bevin that the proposed assembly would, at least at first, have only a consultative role. Things moved ahead slowly and they did not move very far. After yet more British reservations, ten western European nations set up a Council of Europe in May 1949, which would have a Committee of Ministers and a Consultative Assembly. "They have to have something so I'll give them this talking shop," Bevin said.

It had few powers. Its meeting place was in Strasbourg, an appropriate setting for a pan-European body as a French city on the German border with a bilingual population. Its first President was Paul-Henri Spaak. He hoped the Council would become a real supranational body, and resigned after two years when it became clear that it was not going to do so. The Council of Europe set up a Secretariat which performs some technical tasks in European cooperation. Its offshoot is the European Court of Human Rights, which has been given some authority. But it never developed into a United States of Europe or anything like it. The push for European unity that succeeded came from elsewhere.

Britain did take the lead in European unity in another area, defense. The Treaty of Dunkirk signed between Britain and France in 1946 was for defense against a resurgent Germany, but the world had changed in the short time since then. The coup in Czechoslovakia had been alarming. The Soviet Union asked Norway to sign a friendship and cooperation treaty and the Norwegians saw the request as pressure. They were worried that this might lead to Norway becoming another Czechoslovakia.

Bevin sent a memo to Marshall in January 1948 saying that the countries of western Europe should organize for defense with American support. He emphasized intangible factors, sensing, it seems, the low morale in western Europe. "It is not enough to reinforce the physical barriers which still guard our Western civilization," he wrote. "We must also organize and consolidate the ethical and spiritual ... Progress in the economic field will not in itself suffice to call a halt to the Russian threat. Political and indeed spiritual forces must be mobilized in our defence."

He made this idea public with a key foreign policy speech in Parliament on January 22, calling for some kind of union. He said this should start with

France and the Benelux countries, and then "go beyond the circle of our immediate neighbors ... and consider the question of associating other historic members of European civilization, including the new Italy, with this great conception." The speech was welcomed at home and in other European capitals. The *Economist* said, "The Foreign Secretary has set the faltering pulse of Western Europe beating more strongly."

The US Administration also welcomed the idea but seemed to be in no rush to join in. Lovett told Lord Inverchapel that when there was evidence of European unity on defense, and a determination to make it work, then the United States would consider what support it could give. At this time the Administration was struggling to get the ERP Bill through Congress, and it would not have been helpful to suggest to Congress that a further commitment to Europe was in the offing. Bevin told his officials that he was worried that he was caught in a vicious circle. He could not create a western European union without the promise of American support, and America wanted to see a European defense union that was a going concern before committing itself to supporting one.

Bevin put forward a plan for a collective security agreement to the ambassadors of France and the Benelux countries, under article 51 of the United Nations charter. Article 51 provided for nations to band together for collective defense. In those early days of the United Nations its charter was taken very seriously and governments wanted to make sure they were acting in conformity with it.

Talks went ahead. There were difficulties over Germany. France, still obsessed with Germany as a danger, at first wanted the objective of defense against a resurgent Germany written into the treaty. Others objected to this. Although no one said so, some were already looking forward to German participation at some time in the future. Differences were resolved. On March 17, 1948 the five nations signed a mutual defense agreement in Brussels. They agreed to go to one another's aid if one was attacked. There was no mention of who the enemy might be. They set up a military command in Brussels with the British Field Marshal Bernard Montgomery as its commander. This was a new British commitment to the European continent.

From the beginning Bevin wanted full American backing. Just before the treaty was signed he went to see Georges Bidault in Paris and rode with him on the train to the meeting in Brussels. They talked in the carriage with only an interpreter present. Bevin said they should approach the US Government on the basis of its private message of support with the aim of getting America to underwrite the treaty they were about to sign. They should ensure that if war came America would be in it on the first day, and "we would not have to wait for another Pearl Harbor."

President Truman indicated American support immediately and very publicly. He was addressing Congress on a certain day, asking it to expedite the ERP Bill, restore wartime conscription, and introduce a program of universal military training. Then he said:

> At this very moment at which I am addressing you, five nations of the European community in Brussels are signing a fifty-year agreement for economic co-operation and common defense against aggression. This development deserves our full support. I'm sure that the determination of free countries of Europe to protect themselves will be matched by an equal determination on our part to help them protect themselves.

At the first meeting of the treaty's Consultative Council, the French, Belgians, and Dutch suggested a permanent committee to coordinate economic policies. Bidault wanted a political assembly. Despite Bevin's clarion call for a union of European nations, when it came to specifics he continued to hold back. He said economic coordination should be *ad hoc*, and reminded the others that Britain had commitments elsewhere. He was cool in response to the enthusiasm for closer integration. As he told the Council, "One might follow a missionary with zeal, but missionaries do not always lead to salvation."

The idea that western Europe might have to defend itself was gaining ground now, and Soviet behavior strengthened it. In the spring of 1948 the Russians began making life difficult for the Western powers in Berlin. Under the four-power agreement, Berlin was to be governed jointly by the four wartime allies, and the Western powers were to have access by road and rail across East Germany. But then the obstructiveness started: an access road would be closed for repairs one day, and the next all trains would be held up for twelve hours. Then certain railway carriages would be deemed unacceptable. Germans called this "the war of the pinpricks." The build-up of Marshall aid through 1949 took place against a backdrop of increasing East–West tension.

When the Russians were making life difficult for the Western powers in Berlin, Lewis Douglas, the ambassador in London, had a talk with Winston Churchill, then leader of the Conservative Opposition. They talked about Berlin and Churchill suggested a series of countermeasures the Western powers could take. Then he went further. He said that one could not conciliate or appease the Russians, and that once the Soviet Union acquired the atomic bomb, war would be inevitable. He added that while America still had a monopoly on this weapon, it should tell the Soviet Union it must pull out of Berlin and the whole of East Germany or their cities would be razed. Bertrand Russell, the philosopher who went to jail for his pacifism in World War One, and would be imprisoned later for his illegal demonstration against nuclear weapons, wrote an article about this time also advocating preventative war against the Soviet Union.

This was on the wilder shores of Cold War thinking. It is doubtful that Churchill would have carried out such a policy if he were in office. But it reflected a despair about peace which some were coming to feel.

CHAPTER SEVEN

CONFRONTATION

Americans and Europeans traditionally have different attitudes to war. In the American view, certainly in the 1940s before the limited wars that began with Korea, war stands apart from other events in international life and is pursued according to different rules. It is a politics-free zone. In a war one pursues victory without regard to any other goals, and then one goes back to normal life. In this view, "unconditional surrender" is the proper goal in warfare. Roosevelt said unconditional surrender was the Allied aim in World War Two, and this became official policy. It probably prolonged the war, in Europe by denying anti-Hitler Germans the possibility of negotiating a peace with the Allies, and in the Pacific because the Japanese might have surrendered sooner if they had been able to negotiate terms that allowed them to retain their emperor, which they were allowed to do anyway.

Europeans tend to see war in Clausewitzian terms, as "the continuation of politics with the admixture of other means," the extreme end of a spectrum of ways of pursuing national interest, part of a continuing process of international competition. Since international competition will continue after the war, a wise leader looks at how the end of the war will leave the balance of forces, just as a good pool player, aiming to pot a ball, will work out how the table will look after his shot.

Churchill worried about where the end of the war would leave British power, in the Pacific with regard to Britain's empire, and in Europe with regard to the Russians. When Western Allied and Russian armies were pushing into Germany, he wanted, as he said, "to shake hands with the Russians as far to the east as possible." He wanted American and British forces to race ahead and capture Berlin, and Field Marshal Montgomery worked out a tactical plan to do so.

General Eisenhower, with the backing of General Marshall, rejected the idea of racing to Berlin. He took a strictly military view and ignored political considerations. "Berlin has become, so far as I am concerned, nothing but a geographical location," he said. So Soviet troops captured the German capital, after a battle that reduced most of it to rubble, and the hammer and sickle rather than the Stars and Stripes or the Union Jack flew over the Reichstag. Berlin was in the Soviet occupation zone, but it was governed by the four powers.

Germany was the place where World War Two morphed into the Cold War on the ground. Lines were drawn and institutions set up in 1945 to accommodate a situation in which the Soviet Union, the United States, Britain, and France were allies and joint conquerors, and these lines still existed now that they were adversaries. It was as if a field were laid out for football and the players were told that they had to play baseball on it. The situation created anomalies, like the fiction of four-power government of Berlin, and the regular meetings of the four-power Allied Control Council that did not jointly control anything. When Soviet and Western officers clinked glasses at the receptions that one or the other gave, supposedly as joint occupiers, they eyed each other warily.

The occupation authorities, East and West, set up political parties that were in theory all-German parties, but few in the Western zones wanted to join one of the parties in the East operating under Soviet domination, and no one in the Soviet-occupied zone would be allowed to join one of those being established in the Western zones. The zones were governed separately, in ways that reflected to some degree the political stance and character of the occupying powers.

The Kindleberger–Moore–Cleveland memo on European unity (see previous chapter) characterized - even caricatured - the government of the British and American zones: in the US zone, it said, the authorities emphasized free enterprise, and showed "fear if not downright opposition to trade unions, anti-fascist popular fronts, public ownership and similar socialist-type symbols and policies." They supported "the more conservative elements in the community." In the British zone the occupation supported socialism with Germans in control, but it also protected British investments, and developed projects "to find an inordinate number of jobs for British civil servants."

In December 1947 the Western Allies, having given up hope of cooperating with the Russians on governing Germany, met in London to work out a future for the Western zones. They decided that there would be more German self-government leading to a unified West German state. The British and Americans had to argue over this with the French, who still wanted control over the Ruhr and feared a centrally governed West Germany. When Bidault accepted the plan he had to go back to Paris and plead with the National Assembly to support him, warning its members of a serious breach with America and Britain if it did not. Russia objected to the London meeting, arguing that it went against the spirit of four-power cooperation, but this was a dead letter by now anyway.

American troops had been stationed in Germany at the end of the war as occupation forces. Now they were becoming something else, part of the defense of western Europe. Marshall cabled Douglas in London during the conference: "As long as European Communism threatens the U.S. vital interests and national security, we could ill afford to abandon our military position in Germany ... The logical conclusion is that the three-power occupation may be of unforeseeable and indefinite duration."

The German economy was still wrecked. The mark, the all-German monetary unit, had little value; and cigarettes were preferred as currency. Currency reform was the answer, but there was no chance of four-power agreement on this. So in June 1948 the Western Allies announced new deutschmarks for the Western zones. This gave an immediate boost to the German economy, but it also solidified the economic division of Germany between East and West. The Russians objected.

Berlin was divided into four sectors in a mini-version of the division of the country, and small numbers of troops of each occupying power were stationed in its own sector. People could move freely within the city, which limited the degree of Soviet control (the wall cutting the city in two was not erected until 1961). As a response to the London conference, the Russians began the harassment of the British and Americans on the road and rail links across East German territory.

On June 24, the day after the Western Allies announced currency reform, the harassment turned to blockade. The Russians shut down the railway from the west to Berlin, and soon after that closed the roads as well. They gave technical difficulties as the reason, but nobody took that seriously. Berlin was now cut off. It seemed that if the Russians maintained their grip, the Western powers would have to abandon their position in the city. It was a risky strategy for Russia. By apparently confronting the Western powers with the choice of surrendering or resorting to force, it ran the risk of starting a war.

General Clay wanted to send an armored column through to challenge the blockade but this was vetoed because it could lead to shooting. However, Truman was determined that the West should not leave Berlin. He saw the blockade as part of a plan to test the will and capacity of the West to resist. When someone in his cabinet said that the Western position in Berlin was indefensible and they might at least consider the option of withdrawing, he said, "There will be no discussion on this point. We are going to stay, period."

Instead, the US Air Force and the RAF began flying in supplies to the two-and-a-half million people in the western part of the city. They flew Dakotas and C-47 transport planes that were brought in from America. However, this did not seem to be a feasible option in the long term. In normal times, 8,000 tons of supplies were brought in to Berlin daily by road and rail. It was estimated that the minimum for the city to survive was 4,500 tons. By late July, a month after the blockade began, 132 aircraft were each making two flights a day, but they were still bringing in only 2,500 tons each day.

When winter came and the city needed more coal, this figure would rise. On the ground and in the air, men threw themselves into the task and worked to exhaustion, so much so that the commanders were worried about safety and issued an order that men must not make more than two flights without a proper meal.

In August Stalin met the three Western ambassadors to talk about Berlin. US ambassador Walter Bedell Smith said in a dispatch that they had found him "literally dripping with sweet reasonableness" (his use of the word "literally" conjures up a surrealist image). Stalin said the blockade would be lifted if the Western Allies made the Soviet zone deutschmark the currency of all Berlin, and also postponed any further separate arrangements for the Western zones. Bedell Smith was in favor of accepting; he thought the Western Allies would have to abandon Berlin eventually anyway. Bevin argued that giving the Russians control of the currency in Berlin would lead to their control of the city, and Marshall agreed. They rejected Stalin's offer. The blockade must be lifted unconditionally, they said.

The airlift was stepped up. The main Berlin airfield, Tempelhof, was in the middle of the city. The approach carries the aircraft low over buildings, and it is difficult to land when the weather is bad. Berliners, working day and night, built another airfield at Tegel with the longest runway in Europe. Today Tegel is Berlin's principal airport.

When winter came the West Berliners needed more coal and, against expectations, the airlift proved equal to the task. This was partly due to the mild weather, which meant the demand for coal was less than expected. The RAF operation was supplemented by civilian aircraft and crew detached from British European Airways. By the end of the year aircraft were taking in 4,500 tons a day and by the following spring 7,000 tons, with a plane landing every three-and-a-half minutes. At Christmastime the Americans flew in a camel to distribute toys. West Berliners could get by, albeit on short rations.

The three Western powers coordinated their activities through meetings in London between Bevin, the American ambassador Lewis Douglas, and the French ambassador René Massigli. Often these took place in Douglas' office at the American Embassy while Douglas talked on the telephone to Marshall.

At one point in the discussions Bevin said to Charles Bohlen, who was visiting London, "I know you Americans want a war, but I'm not going to let you 'ave one." This was not entirely a joke. Hugh Dalton, the Chancellor of the Exchequer, wrote in his diary, after a conversational lunch with Bevin: "His trouble was to stop the Americans from doing something that would land us in a war." Others held similar views. From Paris David Bruce cabled Washington in September: "The French still fear that American 'boldness' might result in a war in which Russia would only be defeated after French civilization had been destroyed under Soviet occupation." This image of America as a trigger-happy cowboy that needed to be restrained was pervasive. It persisted even when America was using its industrial and technological power, not to fight a war, but to circumvent a challenge.

The British and American public had to get used to hearing Berlin, so recently the evil lair of the enemy, described as an outpost of freedom, and Berliners as brave people defying tyranny. The British Member of Parliament Maurice Edelman reported that when he addressed a local meeting people wanted to know, "Weren't there ever any Nazis in Berlin? Had they all become Communists? If the Russians who were good three years ago are now bad, are the Germans who were bad three years ago now good?"

Fortunately, people in the West found a man they could admire in Berlin's mayor, Ernest Reuter, a Socialist and an anti-Nazi who had spent the war years in exile, a defiant figure wearing the Berlin workman's traditional floppy beret. A one-time Communist who learned his Communism as a prisoner of war in Czarist Russia in World War One, he was now an anti-Communist who encouraged West Berliners to stand firm with defiant speeches.

The West Berliners were indeed defiant, but they were hard pressed, short of food, of coal for their power stations and of petrol for their cars. In the winter they shivered in their homes and sometimes shivered in the dark because of power failures. The only meat they had was tinned and much of their food came in dehydrated form. A cartoon in a Berlin newspaper showed a married couple looking surprised at what the stork has just brought them, a tiny flat baby with a label saying, "Dehydrated. Soak in warm water for twenty minutes."

But they wanted to hold out. Four years earlier, the sound of Allied aircraft had struck terror into the hearts of Berliners. Now, as they struggled through the winter months, the constant sound of the aircraft flying in and out was a reassurance, a lifeline that was being kept open.

In September 1948, after a meeting with Forrestal and others about the Berlin crisis, Truman wrote in his diary, "I have a terrible feeling afterwards that we are very close to war." In Britain, which still had conscription, the Ministry of Defence halted the release of trained men from the services.

The State Department's Policy Planning Staff produced an assessment and concluded that Russia did not want war. It added: "If war comes in the foreseeable future, it will probably be one which Moscow did not desire but did not know how to avoid." The blockade, and the constant friction as British, American, and Soviet troops interacted in the city, created possibilities for an accidental clash. The Russians did not push their action as far as they could have. Most of all, they did not interfere with the air navigation systems over Berlin, which would have made it impossible to operate the airlift.

Much of the press now speculated on the possibility of another war. The *Saturday Evening Post* carried an article titled "If War Comes." *Newsweek* considered an air war with Russia in "White Star vs. Red"; *Time* magazine's headline was tentative: "Russia's War Plan?" William L. Laurence, the science correspondent of the *New York Times*, quoted an unnamed Administration official saying, "If it were not for the atomic bomb, the Russians would be at the Channel right now." This was an image that was taking hold, of a Soviet Army ready to sweep across western Europe, restrained only by the threat of the nuclear bomb.

Scary scenarios were summoned up. At a White House meeting Lovett asked, "If the Communists seized power in the North of Italy, where they're strong, and invite Tito in to help them restore order, what would the United States do?" Opinion polls showed that some 70 percent of Americans thought war was likely in the next ten years.

The US Joint Chiefs of Staff still put the emphasis on deterring aggression. They said in a memo: "The basic objective of defense policy is to convince Russia that war would not pay. However, if this policy fails and a major war should develop, the strategic concept envisages an immediate air offensive, ground defense in Germany as far to the east as possible, an air defense of the countries of the Western union, a defense of the Middle East and North Africa, and finally an offensive on land as soon as possible."

The first fully worked-out American plan for war with the Soviet Union, code-named Half Moon, was produced only in May 1948, and revised in the course of the year. This gave a preeminent role to the atomic bomb. It stated that, in the event of a Soviet offensive in Europe, the United States should respond with an attack with atomic bombs on seventy target areas in the

Soviet Union in which twenty-eight million people lived. The Air Force estimated that 10 percent of these would be killed. However, a review committee headed by Air Force Lieutenant-General H. R. Harmon warned that this might stiffen the Soviet people's will to resist. After all, the Soviet Union had lost twenty million dead in the war.

Truman had little time for the soul searching of Robert Oppenheimer and some of the other scientists who had built the atomic bomb. He had authorized the dropping of the two atomic bombs that ended World War Two and said he never lost any sleep over the decision. But as a humane man he felt revulsion at the weapon. He told David Lilienthal, the first Chairman of the Atomic Energy Commission, "I don't think we ought to use this thing unless we absolutely have to ... You have got to understand that this isn't a military weapon. It is used to wipe out women and children and unarmed people, and not for military uses. So we have got to treat this differently from rifles and cannon and ordinary things like that."

Forrestal, with his aggressive pursuit of military opposition to the Soviet Union, was concerned about this kind of talk, and at one point during the Berlin crisis he pressed Truman on whether he would use the atomic bomb if the Russians attacked in Europe. He reported in his diary, "The President said he prayed he would never have to make such a decision, but that if it became necessary no one need have misgivings about what he would do."

In this world there was little room for the ideals of world government that had inspired many people after the war. Despite the terrifying presence of the atom bomb, conflict had arisen between the great powers, dashing the hopes of many people. Cord Meyer, the former Marine who had devoted himself to the United World Federalists with such energy and commitment, stepped down from the leadership of the organization. He wrote later that it became clear that the big powers were too far apart to create anything like a world government. "There was not a sufficient foundation of shared belief and democratic institutions on which to build the federal structure that was required to contain the nuclear threat," he explained.

He took a fellowship at Harvard and began writing a book about the East–West conflict. He was looking for something else that would take up his energies and would satisfy his resolve, after his wartime experiences, to make the world better.

The British Government was determined to soldier on and not be deflected from its course by Britain's straitened economic circumstances. In April 1948 it introduced the National Health Service, despite Opposition arguments that the country could not afford it. This was at the center of its welfare program. Never again would a British person have to wonder whether he could afford to visit a doctor or go for hospital treatment, never again would a British doctor have to think about whether a patient could afford a particular medicine before he prescribed it. The NHS has been tinkered with in the years since then but its fundamental principles have remained in place.

Like a proud man ignoring the fact that his clothes are threadbare, London hosted the Olympic Games in July 1948, the Government shrugging off the nation's economic plight. This was the first Olympics since those held in Berlin in 1936. Helsinki was to have been the venue for the games in 1940 and London in 1944, but both were cancelled because of the war. The event attracted the usual worldwide attention even though it lacked the extravaganzas that accompanied later games.

Athletes were housed in the RAF barracks in Uxbridge in west London. British participants were given rations equivalent to the heavy-industry worker scale. Many visiting teams had extra food brought in. The Americans had steaks and wholemeal bread flown in and the services of a chef from a top New York hotel. The Soviet Union did not participate because it said it could not afford it. Germany and Japan were not invited.

King George opened the games in Wembley Stadium in sweltering heat which reached 93 degrees Fahrenheit. It was not as big as subsequent Olympics: 4,099 athletes from fifty-eight countries took part, competing in 136 events. The two stars were Bob Mathias, a seventeen-year-old Californian who won the decathlon and became the youngest person ever to win an Olympic gold medal, and Fanny Blankers-Koen, a Dutch housewife who took part in four races and won them all. The Olympics brought thousands of visitors to London and, although they did not find much to eat in the restaurants, this seemed a sign of normality.

When the Russians blockaded Berlin, the US Air Force came back to Britain. Two squadrons of B-29s, the heavy bombers that had come into service too late to see action in the European war and had conducted the air war against Japan, were stationed in the eastern counties. Once again American voices were heard in village pubs in Norfolk and Cambridgeshire. The B-29 was the only bomber capable of carrying an atomic bomb. No atomic bombs were brought to Britain, but loading pits were dug. The aircraft would be positioned over the pit and the bomb would be hoisted into it. The B-29 bases were still designated RAF bases. Later these would expand to a network of US Air Force bases around the country. All but two were closed down in the 1990s, with the end of the Cold War.

The decision to invite the bombers was taken by a small and secret cabinet committee. The aircraft were able to come over quickly because the plans to station them in Britain had been made already. It was not the two governments that drew up the plans; in fact they did not even know about them. The planning had been carried out by the two air force commanders, General Carl A. Spaatz and Air Chief Marshal Lord Tedder.

This was characteristic of British–American relations at the time. Institutionally, there was no special relationship. In the European Recovery Program Britain would be treated like any other European country. There was no formal military agreement. But an arrangement was made informally. The Anglo-American relationship did not rest on written agreements but on the fact that American and British officials found it easy to talk to one another and tended to have a common outlook on things. British people were still foreigners to Americans, and vice versa, but they were less foreign than other foreigners.

When Dean Acheson was Secretary of State, he used to meet regularly with the then British ambassador, Sir Oliver Franks, for confidential, totally informal talks about the international situation. They agreed that both would speak candidly and neither would report on these talks to his government. Such intimacy between a secretary of state and a foreign ambassador is unorthodox and very unusual.

Acheson himself said on one occasion: "Over and over again there comes up this question of our special relationship with the British. It exists. It seems to me to be at the very heart of what we must do to try to hold the world together. But it seems to me more and more something you must know and never speak about." He suited his actions to his words when, in 1950, some State Department officials produced a paper on the special nature of Anglo-American relations. He ordered all copies of the report burned. If the paper got out, he said, it would arouse suspicion among America's allies and provide ammunition to the right-wing isolationists.

At the popular level, this intimacy was not always accompanied by understanding. Transatlantic travel was much rarer than it is today. Few Britons visited the United States; indeed more of them were familiar with India than with America. Most people's views of the other country were shaped by films, which meant *Mrs Miniver*, *A Yank at Oxford*, and comic cockneys for Americans, glamor, cowboys, and gangsters for the British. Britons knew little of America's history.

Both governments recognized the community of interests and outlook. Franks' predecessor in the British Embassy on Massachusetts Avenue, Lord

Inverchapel, wrote when he ended his period as ambassador: "It is virtually taken for granted by responsible Americans that the destinies of Britain and the United States are inseparably bound together by the coincidence of moral and strategic interests. This attitude is particularly marked among members of the Administration, with whom the most pleasant and harmonious relations now exist."

The State Department produces every now and again statements of policy which it circulates among embassies and Washington staff for their guidance. In June 1948 it issued one about Britain. It said:

> Our present policies with respect to the United Kingdom are implemented with the realization that when working together with unity of purpose, the US, the UK and the Commonwealth constitute at present an unequalled force in international affairs. Their people have a common language, heritage and legal system, devotion to the concept of liberty and human rights, and paramount interest in the maintenance of peace. America and Britain as presently constituted are natural allies.

This statement did not limit the common concerns to political interest. It included terms like "moral" and "concept of liberty," because it saw these as factors in the relationship.

The two governments cooperated in the most confidential branch of government, the intelligence services. This cooperation went back to the war years. Americans were admitted to the most secret and the most vital of British wartime intelligence operations, Bletchley Park, where the German armed forces' codes were broken, a project so secret that its existence was not revealed until many years after the war. Britain established a training base in Canada where the fledgling OSS learned something of the dark arts of covert warfare from British intelligence. It also picked up something of the gentleman-adventurer style of the British intelligence service.

When the CIA was created in July 1948, the United States, Britain, Canada, Australia, and New Zealand agreed to share intelligence and to cooperate in intercepting communications. They also agreed not to operate secretly in one another's territory. The bond of trust between the American and British services was strong enough to survive the revelation that the representative in Washington of Britain's Secret Intelligence Service, Kim Philby, privy to many American secrets, was a Soviet agent.

The CIA took up some of the ways of Britain's SIS, such as campus talent-spotters. At Oxford and Cambridge, certain professors were in touch with the SIS and would tip them off about students who might be candidates for the service, who would then be approached. A few professors on American campuses carried out the same function, particularly at Yale, which sent a number of graduates to the CIA as it had to the OSS in wartime.

Despite this intimacy, the changed power relationship created tension, more on the part of the British, who were losing power, than on the part of the Americans. Bevin wrote to Marshall on one occasion welcoming the close relationship, but adding a caveat that could have been uttered by any of his successors over the years: "If in view of this close tie-up, the impression is created that whenever American policy appears to shift we are expected to shift with it, there may well be an outcry at home to the effect that we have sunk to the position of vassal state."

A degree of public hostility was seen in the frequent suspicion of American motives and in the negative stereotyping of Americans as rich, arrogant, insensitive, boastful. One episode was characteristic. It arose from a brush between the popular American view that anything important in the world is done by Americans, always irritating to non-Americans, and British sensitivity. This was the outburst in Britain over the film *Objective Burma.*

Some background to this is needed. The British Fourteenth Army fought a grueling war against one million Japanese troops in the jungles of Burma, driving them back in four years of hard combat. No American ground combat troops were involved, apart from a 2,000-man special forces unit for a short time. British people were mostly watching events in Europe and only after Germany surrendered did attention shift to the war in Burma. The Fourteenth Army was dubbed by the press "the forgotten army," so perhaps a feeling of guilt played a part in what followed.

In the summer of 1948 the film *Objective Burma* opened in London. It was a fairly standard Hollywood war adventure, with a dashing Errol Flynn leading American soldiers fighting the Japanese in Burma. Some popular British newspapers denounced it; they saw it as the Americans claiming credit for a hard-won British victory. People demonstrated angrily at the cinema and the film was withdrawn. The episode lingered for a long time in the popular consciousness, surfacing in remarks like, "Did we really win that battle or was it one of Errol Flynn's?"

The American ambassador in London, Lewis Douglas, found some of this resentment at the official level also in the summer of 1948, and he wrote about it in a dispatch which is worth quoting at length:

> In recent months I have begun to see an undercurrent of feeling here against the U.S. both in and out of government. Sometimes this takes the form of irritation and testiness, but recently it has taken on a much more serious

> form. At times their attitude towards U.S. borders on the pathological, and there have been moments when the feeling here almost resembles an anxiety neurosis. I have tried to get at the bottom of this feeling and offer the following as a possible explanation.
>
> Britain accepts our assumption of world leadership in the face of Russian aggression, and Anglo-American unity is more firmly established than ever before in peacetime. But Britain has never before been in a position where her national security and economic fate are so completely dependent on and at the mercy of another country's decisions. Almost every day brings new evidence of her weakness and dependence on U.S. This is a bitter pill for a country accustomed to full control of her national destiny …
>
> One of the reasons why our relations are subject to severe emotional strain is the quite natural reluctance of Britain to give up her traditional position of world leadership and assume the role of a secondary and dependent power. A second reason is that Britain expects that, in conjunction with Commonwealth and Empire, they will in time regain sufficient strength to deal with the U.S. on relatively equal terms, hence they must avoid, during this period of convalescence, making economic concessions which might impede or interfere with the realization of this expectation.

Douglas noted, with some sympathy, another reason for strained relations: "The British leaders, in government and civil service, are in a state of nervous and physical exhaustion. There is no buoyancy here, no sense of confidence and optimism, of daring and adventure … Britain is subject to pressures of all kinds, internal and external. On top of six years of war she has, since 1947, been living in an atmosphere of continuous economic, political and international crisis, with no slack, no margin of error, no room to maneuver."

The very tone of this message denotes bad feelings among friends, among intimates even, with all the emotional edge that goes with it.

In America, certain phrases from history are venerated and have great power. One thinks of "the right to bear arms," a phrase from the Bill of Rights which applied to the citizens of a largely rural nation of three million inhabitants but which for some today has ultimate authority.

Another such phrase is "avoid entangling alliances." The phrase is usually attributed to George Washington, the first among the founding fathers whose advice is heavy with parental authority, said to come from his farewell address. It was introduced into most foreign policy debates at some point in the two hundred years after George Washington stepped down, and it was the bedrock argument of traditional isolationists. Actually, George Washington did not use this phrase; Thomas Jefferson used it several years later. But it was the message of the foreign policy passage of Washington's address.

"Europe," Washington said, "has a set of primary interests, which to us have none, or a very remote relation. Hence she must be engaged in frequent controversies, the causes of which are essentially foreign to our concerns ... It is our true policy to steer clear of permanent alliances with any portion of the foreign world." Taking this in context, it can be argued that Washington was giving policy advice on this and other matters to be followed for a period until the new republic had expanded and consolidated itself in its new territories. Nevertheless, the United States did avoid any formal alliance with any other country until World War Two, and even then the alliance was short-term and solely for the purpose of prosecuting the war.

Isolationism was the default position for most Americans. So far as they were concerned, their forebears had left Europe to put its quarrels behind them, and they were wiser and luckier than those who remained. International politics was a messy and immoral business and contrary to the American spirit. A bounteous God had given America two oceans for its protection and it did not need to concern itself with what happened on the other side of those seas. World War Two changed this attitude somewhat, and Americans were not going to slide all the way back into their attitude of detachment from the world's affairs, but there was still a reluctance to involve themselves closely.

Actually, America's longtime detachment from world affairs was always something of a myth. Even George Washington in that same farewell address saw the need for an enlarged navy to protect American shipping in the Mediterranean as well as in home waters. The fiercest argument during his Administration was over a treaty with Britain which seemed to favor Britain in its war with France. The Monroe Doctrine, warning foreign powers to stay out of the Americas, was actually a tacit alliance with Britain. It was in Britain's interest as well America's to ensure that no European nation extended its power to the Americas, and President Monroe knew that the British Navy, the most powerful in the world, would ensure that none did.

At the end of the nineteenth century America went into its imperialist phase. It extended its rule to Hawaii and then to the Far East, wresting the Philippines from Spain and then suppressing its independence movement, and it joined the Europeans in imposing economic and trading policies on China. Britain encouraged this. It would rather America expanded into territories ripe for exploitation than France or Germany.

This was the time when the American upper class developed its affinity with the British aristocracy. The most obvious development was a spate of marriages between the daughters of wealthy American families and sons of the British aristocracy. One of these Americans was Jennie Jerome, the daughter of a Wall Street financier and the mother of Winston Churchill. It began to be said at this time that a war between Britain and America was unthinkable for cultural reasons.

Among those in America who concerned themselves with international affairs, a small minority, the predominant view was that America's national interest was the same as Britain's. Britain did not want one power dominating the European continent and nor did America. Thomas Jefferson, despite his earlier enthusiasm for the French Revolution, feared Napoleon as conqueror. In 1814 he wrote, "Surely none of us wish to see Bonaparte conquer Russia, and thus lay at his feet the whole continent of Europe ... It cannot be to our interest that all Europe should be reduced to a single monarchy."

Successive administrations felt that America was safe so long as no single power dominated Europe and the British Navy ruled the Atlantic. The Roosevelt Administration had become alarmed in 1940 when Nazi Germany ruled the continent and it seemed possible that Britain would go down in defeat and the British Navy would disappear from the Atlantic. Now it seemed that there was another threat, from the Soviet Union, and America had a common interest with the nations of western Europe in meeting this threat. Something was needed to institutionalize this common interest.

Bevin wanted to associate America with European defense. Truman had already expressed public approval of the Brussels Treaty of March 1948. Now Marshall, with Truman's approval, wrote a letter marked "top secret" to the British ambassador saying: "Please inform Mr. Bevin that in accordance with your aide mémoire of 11 March, we are prepared to proceed at once in the joint discussions on the establishment of an Atlantic security system. I suggest the prompt arrival of the British representative next week." A spur to everyone was the Communist coup in Czechoslovakia, which had occurred a few weeks earlier.

Bevin responded immediately and two British officials arrived in Washington within days of the signing of the Brussels pact. They met with American and Canadian officials. The British suggested a three-power treaty which the other Brussels Treaty powers would then be invited to join. The Americans did not want a separate treaty with Britain: they suggested instead talks on Atlantic security with the European powers. Kennan and Bohlen, old Soviet hands, were doubtful about the idea. They said it would seem provocative to Moscow, and was unnecessary. They argued that the presence of American troops in Germany ensured that America would have to defend western Europe and the Russians knew this. Although the talks were couched in terms of defense against military attack, the Administration still thought the principal danger was subversion. A State Department paper by John D. Hickerson in March 1948 said: "The problem at present is less one of defense against overt foreign aggression than against internal fifth column aggression supported by the threat of external force, on the Czech model."

The talks were kept secret from the American public and also from Congress. Congress was still debating the ERP Bill - it was passed in April - and this was not a time to suggest to it that another commitment was being considered. But the idea of involving America in Europe's defense was floated by James Reston in the *New York Times* and by Joseph and Stewart Alsop in their syndicated column, and there was no immediate outcry.

Marshall was ill with kidney disease and he delegated most of the work on European defense to James Lovett, who got on well with members of Congress. Lovett got together with Senators Vandenberg and Tom Connally of Texas and they decided that the way ahead was a Senate resolution. Lovett and Vandenberg spent evenings over a typewriter in Vandenberg's apartment at the Wardman Park and together they concocted Senate Resolution 239, usually known as the Vandenberg Resolution. Lovett's part in it was not mentioned. It had to be seen to come from the Senate.

Read quickly it seems like a soufflé of airy ideas about making the world safer. Although there is no mention of Europe or of an alliance or of a treaty, that is what it was about. The resolution asked the President to pursue measures to strengthen the United Nations charter. Then it invited him to support the "development of regional and other collective arrangements for individual and collective self-defense in accordance with the purposes, principles and purposes of the charter." It also asked him to pursue "association of the United States, by constitutional process, with such regional and other collective arrangements as are based on continuous and effective self-help and mutual aid, as affect its national security." Furthermore, the President was to make clear America's "determination to exercise the right of individual or collective self-defense under article 51 should any armed attack occur affecting its national security."

There was no mention of what "collective arrangements" the United States might associate with, nor where the right of "collective self-defense" might be exercised. But it was clear to anyone reading it closely and considering the context that what the author had in mind was a European security arrangement. Not everyone in the Senate did read it closely. Vandenberg's aide

Francis Wilcox said privately when it was up before the Senate, "Most senators don't know what they're voting on." What they were voting for, whether they realized it or not, was whether to give an American president the go-ahead to join a European defense pact. The Senate passed the Resolution by 64 votes to 4.

Charles Bohlen wrote later: "The resolution marked the end of American isolationism, since it was the first time in history that any such idea had emanated from Washington, and certainly the first time Congress had approved of such a move." It was to lead to America's first real entangling alliance.

Any talks in Washington about future arrangements that summer were going to be cautious. This was an election year, and the forecasts were that the next president would be a Republican. However, under Truman the major foreign policy initiatives had been bipartisan. The only leading Republican who might be expected to change America's course if he became president was Senator Taft, and at the convention in July he lost his bid for the nomination to Thomas Dewey, who had run against Roosevelt in 1944. Dewey accepted the main planks of the Administration's foreign policy. The debating points between the two parties were all domestic.

Nonetheless, the Administration was not going to commit its successor to a major new move, particularly with a Republican Congress. Foreign ambassadors and even senior State Department men who wanted to keep their jobs were talking tentatively to the likely coming men in a Republican administration. Principal among these was John Foster Dulles, who was expected to be Dewey's choice as Secretary of State; he had been involved in early discussions on aid to Europe and in some of the most active elements of the Truman Administration's foreign policy.

The Republican-dominated Congress approved successive aid measures and the Marshall Plan because the Administration managed to insulate these issues from the arguments over domestic policy. On these the Administration and Congress often collided. The Republicans in the House of Representatives in particular were conservatives who had dreamed for years of rolling back Roosevelt's New Deal. Truman had wanted economic controls which would hold down prices. Congress threw out his proposals. Truman vetoed several bills passed by Congress. The Taft–Hartley labor bill, which banned the closed shop and restricted the right to strike, was passed over his veto. He blocked a move to reduce taxes which he said would benefit the wealthy and cut into welfare programs. Truman's relationship with the Eightieth Congress was an adversarial one. He did not only disagree with Congress, he lambasted it. He called it a "do-nothing" legislature, and said it was controlled by "the special-interest boys."

His most far-reaching proposal to Congress was over civil rights. He started moving on the issue when he addressed the National Association of Colored People, the mainstream organization pressing for Afro-American rights, something no president had done before. In a speech that was broadcast nationally, he declared that the Government must lead the way in guaranteeing equality of treatment in education, housing, and medical care, and in protection from discrimination. He gave his approval to a report by a government-appointed Civil Rights Committee advocating a wide range of measures. He held back for the moment from pushing these, partly because Congress was still debating the ERP and the support of Southern senators and congressmen was important. But he had staked out his position.

It was a bold one. Racial segregation was enforced by law in the Southern states, where there were separate schools, hospitals, and even park benches and drinking fountains for whites and non-whites. Arthur Miller recalled that when, as a young man visiting South Carolina, he addressed an elderly Afro-American as "Sir," he received a sharp rebuke; he was told that he should have called him "Boy." Elsewhere segregation in many areas of life was supported by custom. Truman's position was anathema to most in the South. His sister back in Missouri, Mary Jane Truman, was disbelieving. She told a reporter: "Harry's no more in favor of nigger equality than I am." Even in the rest of the country, although the President's position enjoyed strong backing from liberals, opinion polls showed only a minority in favor.

Truman's approval rating was falling. He had been a popular president in 1947, but in April 1948 a Gallup poll showed that only 36 percent approved of him as president. He was compared often and unfavorably with Roosevelt, in stature and gravitas. He was seen as a politician rather than a statesman.

At the Democratic Party convention in Philadelphia in July, he was nominated as presidential candidate while the band played "I'm Just Wild about Harry," which became his campaign song. Truth to tell, the Democratic Party was not wild about him. He seemed like an election loser. But rejecting the incumbent and choosing someone else as candidate would mean certain defeat, and besides, there was no serious challenger. There had been talk of drafting Eisenhower as Democratic candidate but Eisenhower brushed this aside.

As it turned out, this convention set in motion events that would change American politics for ever. The liberal wing of the party insisted on a platform including the entire program of civil rights legislation that Truman had put before Congress. Delegates from Southern states rebelled. The deep South states were solidly Democrat, for reasons of history rather than ideology; the Republicans were the party of Abraham Lincoln and the anti-slavery forces, and the South had voted against Lincoln ever since the civil war. Most of the states of the old Confederacy were in effect one-party states. In any one of these, the fight for a seat in Congress was decided by the fight for the Democratic Party nomination, which guaranteed election. Under Roosevelt the South, largely rural, racist, and socially conservative, formed an uneasy coalition in the Democratic Party with the liberal and labor elements in the Northern states who were the main supporters of Roosevelt's New Deal.

When the 1948 convention voted to include the civil rights plank in the platform, the Mississippi delegation walked out, accompanied by half the delegates from Alabama and a number of others. These decided to enter the campaign as a third party, the States Rights Party, with J. Strom Thurmond, the Governor of South Carolina, as their candidate for the presidency. They became known as the Dixiecrats. If the Dixiecrats could win three or four states, they thought this might create a tie, which would throw the election to the House of Representatives. The Dixiecrats' defection left its mark. The solid South, as political observers called it, was no longer so solid. There was another Dixiecrat defection over civil rights in the 1960 election when Kennedy was the Democratic candidate, and since then the deep South states have no longer been one-party but have been up for grabs and have often voted Republican.

Another new party entered the presidential race, the Progressive Party, campaigning on a platform of friendship with the Soviet Union with Henry Wallace as the candidate. Now the political calculus had swung against Truman. Both the new parties would take votes away from the Democrats, the Dixiecrats on the right, the Progressive Party on the left.

Thomas Dewey, the Republican candidate, was good-looking and clearly competent but uninspiring. Alistair Cooke skewered him in the *Manchester Guardian*: "He has gone after the presidency with the humorless calculation of a certified public accountant going after the Holy Grail." Nevertheless, everything was going, if not for Dewey, then against Truman. Throughout the campaign the opinion polls forecast a Republican victory and the political pundits agreed to a man.

Truman was not a good speaker when he was reading from a prepared script, but he was effective in speaking off the cuff. His advisors told him to play to his strength. Instead of trying to appear statesmanlike, he would put himself across as the ordinary American sharing the concerns of other Americans. If he appeared to lack gravitas, he would abandon any attempt at it.

He criss-crossed the country three times in a railroad train, sometimes delivering three or four speeches and stopping at five or six other small towns for a brief visit in one day, exhausting reporters travelling with him who were half his age (he was sixty-four). He spoke as he felt to small crowds and large crowds, in small towns where leafy branches hung over the little railway station and in big city terminals, against a background of snow-capped mountains or endless flat cornfields. He did not speak in the shade of magnolia trees. He avoided the deep South states, where he would not have been welcome.

"Give 'em hell, Harry," someone called out from his audience, and this became the theme of his campaign. He was feisty and combative. He called Dewey and the Republicans "errand boys for big business." He did not just ask people to vote for him. He asked them to vote out the Republican Congress with whom he had battled. "You've got the worst Congress you ever had, and if you send another Republican Congress to Washington you're a bigger bunch of suckers than I think you are," he said in Ohio. In Oakland, California, he advised his crowd: "Fire the Congress, a bunch of Eastern Republican mossbacks." Projecting a homely image, he always introduced his wife Bess, "the boss," and his daughter Margaret, "who bosses the boss." As a one-time farmer he showed people he was at one with rural America. In Iowa he told people he measured a crowd in acres. In a small town in Oklahoma he opened a horse's mouth, looked at its teeth and guessed its age correctly. Reporters estimated that three million people saw Truman speak.

A Gallup poll on election eve showed Dewey with 49.5 percent of the vote and Truman with 44.5 percent. *Life* magazine carried a portrait of Dewey with the caption "The next President." Political forecasters were unanimous in giving the election to Dewey and the Republicans.

The result was the most stunning political upset in American history. Truman won, even though the Dixiecrats carried three states. The first edition of the *Chicago Tribune* proclaimed in a banner headline, "Dewey Beats Truman," and a grinning Truman was photographed holding it up. Today that edition is a collectors' item.

More than that: the voters had done what Truman has asked them to do and given him a Democratic Congress. The Democrats won back control of both Houses. Truman now had greater freedom to go ahead with plans to commit America to engagement with the wide world and could expect less obstruction from Congress.

CHAPTER EIGHT

COMMITTED AND ENTANGLED

With hindsight, the division of Europe into two armed camps in longterm confrontation seems inevitable, a natural consequence of the triumph of Communism in one group of nations and its rejection by another. It did not seem inevitable at the time. When the project for a North Atlantic defense pact was being discussed in Washington, George Kennan, a political thinker of the realist school who could hardly be accused of starry-eyed optimism about Russia, wrote a paper expressing the hope that this could be avoided. "It may not be possible for us to prevent a congealment of the present lines of division," he wrote.

> But our present policy is still directed (and in the opinion of the staff rightfully so) towards the eventual peaceful withdrawal of both the United States and the U.S.S.R. from the heart of Europe, and accordingly towards the encouragement of the growth of a third force which can absorb and take over the territory between the two.
>
> Unless we are prepared to depart from this policy, to renounce hopes of a peaceful solution of Europe's difficulties, and to plan our foreign policy deliberately on the assumption of a coming military conflict, we should not do things which tend to fix, and make unchangeable by peaceful means, the present line of east–west division.

Despite Kennan's strictures, talks on a North Atlantic security pact began in September 1948, between the five Brussels pact members and Canada, represented by their ambassadors, and the US State Department, represented by Lovett, and later by Acheson. They were held in private, and in any case American newspapers were taken up mostly with the Presidential election campaign.

Lovett started in a low key, determined not to raise expectations. He said the United States could not sign a pact that committed it to go to war because only Congress could declare war. He also pointed out that from the point of view of America's own security, Iceland and Greenland were more important than the Benelux countries. He made it clear that nothing was going to be decided quickly. He told the others they could expect no American action until after the election in November, in fact not until the new session of Congress in January the following year.

The participants decided early on what the terms of the treaty would be. The essential sentence said: "An armed attack by any state against a party [to the treaty] shall be considered an attack on all parties." This represented a historic change in America's stance in the world, binding its fate to that of other countries. It was not a commitment to be reached in private and then simply offered to the Senate for approval. Lovett involved senior members of the Senate from the beginning, an unusual procedure.

The participants decided that associating America with the Brussels pact was not enough, that a larger group of countries was needed, a North Atlantic treaty. They said they would welcome as members Norway, Denmark, Iceland, Ireland, and Portugal, all Atlantic countries.

The Norwegian Government had before it a proposal from Sweden for a Scandinavian bloc of these two countries plus Denmark. But it would be a neutral bloc. Norway would have to choose. The Foreign Minister, Halvard Lange, came to Washington to discuss it. A veteran of the Norwegian resistance movement and of Dachau concentration camp, he said that Norway's experience in the war indicated that neutrality was not sustainable. His Government agreed and chose the Atlantic Pact.

Portugal posed a problem since it was a dictatorship. The British cabinet discussed this, and Bevin said it was less objectionable than Spain and, strategically, they needed the Azores, the Portuguese islands in the Atlantic. So Portugal was invited. The Irish Government replied to the invitation with a message reflecting its overriding historic concern, saying it would join the pact only as a united Ireland.

France wanted Italy to be a member. Military men argued that Italy would not contribute to the defense of western Europe and might be a drain on resources. It was not a North Atlantic country. But the State Department wanted Italy in the treaty to bind it more closely to the West and it was decided to invite Italy. Greece and Turkey said that if Italy were admitted they wanted to be also. The State Department tried to mollify them by pointing out that America was already committed to their defense.

France also wanted Algeria to be included in the area covered by the pact. This raised anxieties among the others. If Algeria came in, would not other countries want their colonial territories in Africa to be included as well? After some discussion the meeting accepted Algeria, because it was constitutionally a part of France, but not France's other North African territories, Morocco and

Tunisia. The French ambassador at the talks, Georges Bonnet, insisted that Russia was not the only danger, that a revived Germany might again threaten its neighbors one day.

In the paper containing his thoughts on the proposed Atlantic pact, Kennan addressed a paradox: the treaty was designed to meet the danger of military aggression, but that was not the principal danger facing western Europe. Kennan wrote:

> It is important to understand that the conclusion of such a pact is not the main answer to the present Soviet effort to dominate the European continent ... The danger of political conquest is still greater than the military danger. If a war comes in the foreseeable future, it will probably be one which Moscow did not desire but did not know how to avoid. The political war, on the other hand, is now in progress; and if there should not be a shooting war, it is this political war which will be decisive.
>
> A North Atlantic security pact will affect the political war only insofar as it operates to stiffen the self-confidence of the Western Europeans in the face of Soviet pressure. Such a stiffening is needed and desirable. But it goes hand in hand with the danger of a general preoccupation with military affairs, to the detriment of economic recovery and of the necessity for seeking a peaceful solution to Europe's difficulties.

When it came to the specifics, Kennan did not think Italy should be admitted. He also worried that the admission of Norway would be crowding Russia. (One wonders what he would think of NATO today, including as it does former members of the USSR right along Russia's European frontier.)

The Communists opposed NATO everywhere, as had been expected. When the issue was debated in the Italian Chamber of Deputies the debate went on for fifty-two hours, the longest debate in the Chamber in postwar history, with the left opposing it, and it erupted at times into fistfights before the measure was passed.

When the British cabinet discussed the treaty, Bevin, whose goal this had been, expressed what had become his usual worries about becoming too closely involved with other European countries. Like a commitment-phobic man on a date, he wanted the alliance but he was insistent that it be limited. He said they should resist any attempt to extend the North Atlantic Treaty beyond defense to include economic, social, or cultural areas. Most members of the cabinet were at one with him in this. When, later, Canada wanted to insert an article in the treaty on cultural links, Bevin agreed reluctantly but assured the cabinet that this would have no practical effect.

Soon after the talks began the Democrats won their election victory. The European participants had not been worried about the result since the main aspects of foreign policy were bipartisan. Nonetheless, they were relieved that they would be dealing with the same people.

One person was leaving the scene. General Marshall's kidney disease was becoming incapacitating. Three days after his inauguration President Truman announced that Marshall was resigning, and would be succeeded as Secretary of State by Dean Acheson. Marshall was awarded the Nobel Peace Prize in 1953. There was another change. With the Democrats in control of the Senate, Vandenberg was no longer majority leader but minority leader.

The senators involved in the talks were worried about the wording of the treaty, and in particular the question of what came to be known in the discussions as "automatic involvement." The senators could not accept a treaty that would automatically involve the United States in a war, since only Congress could declare war. Vandenberg, who wanted the treaty, saw this as a dilemma. The more specific the commitment, the more opposition there was likely to be in the Senate. The more vague it was, the less strength it would have to reassure the European members and deter a potential aggressor.* They settled on a clause stating that in the event of aggression members would take "such action as each deems necessary," which was less than automatic commitment. They strengthened it by adding the words "including the use of armed force."

The text was published simultaneously in the capitals of the twelve prospective member countries in March 1949. When it was debated in the Senate only a few senators opposed it. Tom Connally was one of these. He said the pact might mean "letting Europeans declare war and letting us fight." He went on, "We cannot, every time we hear a gun being fired, plunge into war and take sides without knowing what we are doing and without knowing the issues involved." But most of the senators had no such worries and the Senate ratified the treaty with only ten dissenting votes.

The foreign ministers of the twelve member countries assembled in Washington to sign the North Atlantic Treaty on April 4. A few of the more cynical among those present snickered at the significance they saw in two of the songs that the Marine band played during the signing, from George and Ira Gershwin's musical play *Porgy and Bess*. They saw a comment on the fragility of international guarantees in "It Ain't Necessarily So," and on the paucity of military strength to back up the treaty in "I Got Plenty of Nothin'."

* It was the Senate's fear that America might be automatically committed to go to war that had made it reject membership of the League of Nations in 1920.

Just a few hours after the signing ceremony, President Truman set out to remedy this military weakness in Europe. He asked Congress to authorize $1.4 billion in military aid, most of it to go to America's new European partners. Although he had a Democratic Congress now, it was in a fractious mood that summer, and members of both Houses argued about the bill, first demanding that the President's powers of discretion be reduced, which was done, and then arguing about the sum, which was reduced and then largely restored.

No amount of military assistance that was feasible was going to enable the creation of forces in western Europe to match the Soviet forces. The Soviet Union had four times the forces in Germany that America and Britain had, plus the armies of its satellite countries. Most of the French regular army was fighting in Indochina, in a war that would end with France's expulsion in 1954. The Administration knew it was not possible, for budgetary and other reasons, to try to match the Soviet Union in strength on the ground in Europe. Acheson explained what they were trying to achieve: "The result attainable would be a force in Europe that would preclude a quick victory by sudden marches, backed up by an American capability for punishing blows against an aggressor's home territory." This placed the emphasis on deterrence.

In May the Russians agreed to end the blockade of Berlin, after eleven months. Western determination had paid off. The only *quid pro quo* was a nominal one: another four-power foreign ministers' meeting to discuss Germany. This took place later the same month in Paris, in the Palais Rouge. With Germany now divided, the Western governments did not expect much to come out of the meeting so they were not disappointed. The Western powers proposed all-German elections, which the Russians rejected.

The wrangling over the agenda, the tediousness of listening to every speech three times, once in the original and twice in translation, created a mood of exasperation and provoked some ill-tempered exchanges. At one point Andrei Vishinsky, who was now the Soviet Foreign Minister, said they should meet in the afternoons and evenings. Bevin replied that if they met in the evening Vishinsky's long speeches would put him to sleep. Vishinsky retorted that something seemed to put Bevin to sleep in the afternoons anyway. Bevin said he recommended the practice as it helped one get through the meetings.

The NATO Council met for the first time in Washington in September 1949. In the same month the Federal German Republic came into existence in the American, British, and French occupation zones, after an election which had a 78.5 percent turnout, with Konrad Adenauer as the first Chancellor. It was not yet independent; the Allied High Commission, representing the three occupying powers, still had the right of veto over its legislation, and Adenauer had to take bills passed by the Bundestag to the Commission for its approval. The following month the German Democratic Republic, in effect a Communist dictatorship, was established in the Soviet zone.

One group of people within a nation is always at war. An intelligence service spies on other countries, particularly those that it identifies as potential enemies. Until World War Two, the United States had no overseas intelligence service. Henry Stimson, when he was Secretary of State under President Hoover, closed down the State Department's code-breaking department saying, "Gentlemen do not read one another's mail." Later, however, Americans cracked the Japanese naval code before Pearl Harbor, which could have given warning of the attack.

During the war the OSS developed into an intelligence service among other things, but Roosevelt insisted that there must be no espionage activities directed against Russia, America's ally. When the OSS acquired top-secret Soviet code-books from the Finns, Roosevelt instructed the OSS Director, William Donovan, to give them back. Donovan did so, but he made a copy first.

At the end of the war in Europe some American and British Army intelligence units began seeking information on the Soviet Union, using German intelligence officers as sources. The Russians were doing the same in reverse. Both sides recruited intelligence sources in secret as scientists were being recruited semi-publicly, Werner von Braun, who became head of the American space program, being the best known. The Americans and British employed whoever would provide useful intelligence, in a few cases allowing war criminals to escape justice in exchange for their help. One of the beneficiaries was Klaus Barbie, the notorious Gestapo chief in Lyons, who was brought back from Bolivia and tried for war crimes in France only in 1983.

In 1948, after the Czech coup, Truman signed the secret NSC Directive 10/2. This went beyond espionage to covert warfare. It called for psychological warfare and also allowed for "economic warfare, sabotage and ... subversion against hostile states, including assistance to underground resistance movements." It added that any such activities must be carried on in such a way that the Government could plausibly deny any involvement. George Kennan had proposed such a course to the Administration. While his containment policy was criticized by some for being too defensive, he was urging offensive operations in secret. He said the aim would be not to overthrow the Soviet Government but "to create circumstances that would make it difficult for the present Soviet leadership to retain its power," and it would take a very subtle mind to distinguish between these two objectives.

The Director of the newly established CIA was Rear Admiral Roscoe K. Hillenkoetter. Hillenkoetter would have nothing to do with such activities. He said the CIA was designed to gather and collate intelligence. It would engage in espionage and even run some propaganda operations, but would "stop short of the physical" – that is, sabotage or paramilitary operations.

So the State Department set up a deliberately obscure and innocuous-sounding group called the Office of Policy Coordination, the OPC. It was headed by Frank Wisner, an old OSS hand who had seen the Soviet take-over of Romania, and a few others from the OSS, many of them wealthy and well connected socially. They recruited others from Ivy League campuses for this new underground war. One recruit was William Colby, a former OSS man who had been parachuted into German-occupied France and Norway and who would later become Director of the CIA; he recalled "the atmosphere of an order of Knights Templar to save Western Freedom from Communist darkness." Richard Bissell saw it as an adjunct to the Marshall Plan, operating alongside it. "It was a complementary operation to save Western Europe," he said. There was a financial connection. The OPC funded its activities in Europe from the 5 percent of Marshall aid counterpart funds that were set aside for American activities in Europe.

Few people in the State Department or anywhere else knew about the OPC and fewer still knew what it did. It was the OPC that funneled money to anti-Communists in Italy during the Italian election campaign, and to the liberal left in France. It was the OPC that took the first steps in recruiting eastern European anti-Communist émigrés to operate in Communist countries. The OPC fought Communism on the intellectual front. The Communists in their propaganda were donning the mantle of peace, assigning the Western leaders the role of aggressors. A lot of people seemed to be going at least some way along with this. Prominent intellectuals attended the Cultural and Scientific Conference for World Peace at the Waldorf Astoria Hotel in New York, including Albert Einstein and Charles Chaplin, with Picasso sending good wishes. The Conference, like some conferences and organizations that followed, was less strident than overt Soviet proaganda, but it conveyed the impression that the danger of war lay in Western leaders' attitudes. Peace was a good horse to mount. In the age of the atomic bomb, who was not appalled at the thought of war?

To counter this the OPC helped set up the Congress for Cultural Freedom, which gathered together anti-Communist and often ex-Communist intellectuals. It funded in secret intellectual magazines with a liberal tendency such as *Encounter* in Britain, *Preuves* in France, and *Der Monat* in Germany. It funded the National Committee for a Free Europe, a supposedly private New York-based organization of anti-Communist émigrés from eastern Europe and their American well-wishers. This in turn created Radio Free Europe, a major broadcasting service beamed at countries behind the Iron Curtain and broadcasting in eastern European languages, supposedly supported by money raised from the public but actually funded by OPC, a role later taken over by the CIA.

The OPC also went physical, to use Admiral Hillenkoetter's term. In Europe it organized "stay behind" groups who were prepared to go into action if Soviet armies overran western Europe. The program was run by Frank Lindsay, who, as an OSS officer, had fought with Tito's partisans in German-occupied Yugoslavia. An old hand with explosives, he organized people to carry out what the OPC called "retardation," mining bridges and roads, and to remain in touch for purposes of espionage.

In 1949 the OPC began conducting covert warfare against the Soviet Union. It exploited the nationalist resentment of people among the ethnic minorities in the Soviet Union, and also of people in the Baltic states that had been forcibly incorporated into the Soviet Union in 1940 – Estonians, Lithuanians, and Latvians. (These nations and others finally achieved independence with the break-up of the USSR in 1989–91.) During the war the West was given a picture of the Soviet people united in resisting the German invaders, but in fact when the war ended more than half a million Soviet citizens were serving the German forces, many of them Ukrainians or Belorussians. Large numbers of those fled to the West, some to be forcibly repatriated. Others remained in the Soviet Union as wanted men and waged guerrilla warfare in the forests. The OPC and later the CIA contacted members of these groups in Germany. This meant immersing themselves in émigré politics, with their internecine quarrels. Many Ukrainian nationalists would have nothing to do with any Russians, even anti-Communists. Alexander Kerensky, the last democratically elected Russian Prime Minister, overthrown by the Bolsheviks in the 1917 Revolution and now living in California, denounced one American-sponsored group of émigré Russians.

They trained groups in espionage and sabotage and dropped them by parachute into the Soviet Union, and they infiltrated anti-Communists into other eastern European countries. These were recruited for their anti-Communist zeal rather than for any other qualities. Some Romanians infiltrated into their homeland were prewar members of the Iron Guard, which had matched the Nazis in its persecution of liberals and Jews in enthusiasm if not efficiency. Some Ukrainians were members of a group nicknamed the Nightingales, who served the SS in German-occupied Ukraine and hunted down Jews and partisans for them.* The operations extended over three years and were an almost total failure. Most of the hapless men landed in their own countries were captured and executed. Their activities doubtless contributed to Soviet suspicion of Western intentions.

This was full-spectrum covert warfare, precisely what James Burnham had urged on the West in his book *The Struggle for the World*. Burnham was teaching at New York University but an old Princeton classmate recruited him for the OPC and he moved to Washington. Here he was given a chance to practise what he had preached. He gave advice on which anti-Communist groups to support, suggested propaganda lines to follow, and planned disinformation and subversion campaigns.

Sometimes the US Government's deniability wore thin. An American Air Force plane forced down over Hungary carried spare parachutes, detailed maps of the Volga region, and local currency. Sometimes the politics were inept. Three anti-Communists émigrés were parachuted into Yugoslavia and captured almost immediately. The American ambassador to Belgrade, Cavendish Cannon, was furious. American policy was to support Yugoslav President Tito in his quarrel with Stalin.

The British and Americans cooperated in a project to topple Albania's Communist Government. This had Bevin's personal approval. Albania was a small country, with a population of less than two million, and was isolated from the rest of the Soviet bloc. Albanian anti-Communists were landed by boat from Cyprus. Others were trained in Germany and parachuted in. All were rounded up almost immediately. One of the British planners on the operation was Kim Philby, the SIS officer who was a longtime Soviet spy.

Later, all these activities were brought together under the CIA, which had shed Admiral Hillenkoetter's inhibitions. Like the Pentagon, which was established at the same time, the CIA became an arm of America's overseas operations as America extended its reach across the world.

When the ECA was wound up Richard Bissell went to work for the Ford Foundation, but he hankered after life at the center. At the ECA he had met

* The employment of such people presumably set up a conflict in the minds even of committed anti-Soviet activists like William Forrestal, who as Secretary of Defense would have known about these operations. His biographer speculates that the recollection of the Nightingales might have contributed to Forrestal's suicide in 1949. He was in a psychiatric hospital following a mental breakdown and was copying out a translation of a poem by Sophocles, in which Ajax contemplates suicide. He came to the phrase "the querulous nightingale" but wrote only the syllable "night," put down his pen, and leaped from a seventh-floor window.

Frank Wisner, and had handed over to him counterpart funds to use for OPC operations. They were both Yale men, and they moved in the same social circles in Washington. Wisner told his boss, CIA Director Allen Dulles, about Bissell and Dulles approached him at a dinner party given by the journalist Stewart Alsop and offered him a job. Bissell went into the clandestine operations division and showed talent in this area, helping to plan the coup that overthrew the Guatemalan Government in 1954. He took part in plots against Fidel Castro and was one of the organizers of the ill-fated Bay of Pigs invasion of Cuba in 1963. After this fiasco he was eased out of the agency.

The idealism of Cord Meyer, the young ex-Marine who had founded the United World Federalists and wanted global government, could not survive in this world of struggle. He had already decided that there was not enough common ground among the big powers to allow world federalism and he abandoned the movement. He remembered what he had felt in the Pacific, that he owed it to his dead comrades to do what he could to "make the future for which they had died an improvement on the past." But his view of what needed to be done had changed.

He contacted the State Department but found his past activities were an impediment to employment there. Once again social connections paved the way. He approached Allen Dulles. "We had a number of friends in common at whose houses we played tennis on Long Island weekends," he explained later. He joined the CIA and rose to be head of the Directorate of Plans, and waged the secret war with a will. He was involved in the program to subsidize anti-Communist publications and Radio Free Europe. When the left-wing Arbenz Government took power in Guatemala he tried to keep pro-Arbenz articles out of American newspapers. He worked on a number of covert operations, and for a time was the CIA representative in London. Tom Braden, who worked with him in the CIA, says he became "a true believer in the fight against diabolical Communism."

Meyer ran a program to subsidize the National Association of Students so that they could send American students to international gatherings to counter the Communist point of view. The students who went were unaware of the source of their funding. Some people were outraged when this was exposed by the magazine *Ramparts* in 1967, but one of those who went, the feminist writer Gloria Steinem, said, "Far from being shocked at this involvement, I was happy to find some liberals in government who cared enough and were far-sighted enough to get Americans of all political views at these festivals."

Tragedy and scandal entered Meyer's life. One of his three sons, nine-year-old Michael, was knocked down and killed by a car. He and his wife Mary

Pinchot were divorced, and in 1964 she was shot dead when she was out jogging. Her killer was never found. After her death it was revealed that she had had an affair with President Kennedy. James Jesus Angleton, the head of CIA counter-intelligence, was found breaking into her house, and he explained that he was looking for her diary. Conspiracy theories grew up linking her with CIA drug experiments and with President Kennedy's assassination.

At one point during the period of anti-Communist excesses, the FBI labeled Meyer a security risk, citing his early involvement in liberal causes, and he was suspended from his post. Allen Dulles, unlike his brother John Foster Dulles, was vigorous in defending his employees when they came under unjustified suspicion, and Meyer was reinstated after an inquiry.

After he retired he wrote an autobiography, *Facing Reality*. He portrayed a Manichean world, with the CIA battling the evil forces of Communism represented by the KGB, which was always better funded and had fewer scruples. He deplored moves which have clipped the wings of the CIA. Where the CIA intervened in other countries, it was always for the world's benefit. He fought the Cold War with a will. There are in the book no nuances, no grey areas, no suggestion of sometimes having to choose between evils, all of which make up the reality of international life. In the short story he wrote in 1946 about the Pacific war, he has a soldier reflecting:

> It would have been better for man, he felt, if he had been given no trace of gentleness, no desire for goodness, no capacity for love. These qualities were all he valued but he could see they were the pleasant illusions of children. With them men hoped, struggled pitifully, and were totally defeated by an alien universe in which they wandered as unwanted strangers. Without them an animal, man, might happily eat, reproduce and die, one with what is.

Gentleness and the capacity for love are not the qualities required for a warrior. Perhaps Cord Meyer, if he was going to fight the Cold War, and in fact live in the world that he found, had to suppress these qualities in himself. These qualities are indeed difficult to sustain in a world of struggle, and perhaps possessing these qualities to too fine a degree must always make one vulnerable. So in most of us they are often suppressed, or dismissed as "the pleasant illusion of children." If this was Cord Meyer's tragedy, it is ours also.

The issue of Anglo-American cooperation on nuclear weapons never entirely disappeared. In January 1949 the British Government made a new proposal for an exchange of information. The two countries were already cooperating on uranium supplies, most of which at this stage were coming from the

Belgian Congo. All of it was going to the United States for the moment because Britain had enough. The arrangement was due to run out at the end of 1949 and something else had to replace it. Truman appointed a committee to look into the question, composed of leading figures from the State and Defense Departments and the Atomic Energy Commission, and General Eisenhower. This recommended full cooperation on both civil and military nuclear power with Britain and Canada.

Britain was going full speed ahead to develop an atomic bomb and atomic power for civilian purposes, and it would continue to do so with or without American help. The Administration was told that Britain would have its first nuclear reactor in operation within a year, and it would have a bomb in four years at the latest without American help or in two-and-a-half years with it.

Truman approved the committee's recommendation, but they came up against Congress. He and the committee members met with the Joint Congressional Committee on Atomic Energy. Acheson led off with the proposal for full cooperation. He was backed up vigorously by Eisenhower. Eisenhower said America's military situation was so bound up with Britain's now that it made no sense to exclude one weapon from the scope of their partnership. He said the attempt to do so was already poisoning the trust between the countries and could jeopardize the relationship.

Members of Congress were not receptive. Senator Vandenberg was the first to object. He said America was constantly bailing Britain out, and was being asked to do so again with atomic weapons. Truman told him that the information America would be giving to Britain would be no more valuable than the information America would receive. Others pointed to the greater efficiency to be obtained by cooperation. Well then, Vandenberg said, the answer was for America to be the sole producer of atomic weapons and to allocate some to Britain. Acheson invited him to put himself in the position of a British prime minister, on the verge of producing his own atomic bombs, being asked to abandon the program and rely on the United States. Vandenberg saw the point.

There were two other meetings. Defense Secretary Louis Johnson was adamantly opposed to cooperation with Britain, as were some senators. They were less resistant after Russia exploded its first atomic bomb in September of that year. Discussions with British officials went ahead. The two governments agreed on the allocation of uranium supplies.

The British seemed ready to acquiesce in the fabrication of atomic weapons being concentrated in America and an agreement to cooperate was in sight. Then, in Acheson's words, "a bomb exploded in London." Klaus Fuchs, one of the heads of Britain's Atomic Research Centre at Harwell, was arrested and charged with espionage. It turned out that he had been sending information on the atomic bomb to Russia, and had been doing so when he worked on the wartime atomic bomb project in America. The talks went into deep freeze.

Two events changed the global balance of power in the last part of 1949. One was Russia's explosion of its nuclear bomb in September. Western governments had assumed that Russia was working on a bomb but estimated that it would not produce one for another two years at least. The information supplied by Klaus Fuchs was a great help; the best guess among scientists was that it saved Russia a year to eighteen months. The United States still had a substantial lead in the numbers of atomic bombs, but this lead would dwindle and become less significant. The atomic bomb is a great equalizer.

The second was the Communist victory in the Chinese Civil War in the following month. Chiang Kai-shek and his Government fled to Taiwan and Mao Tse-tung stood in Tiananmen Square and announced the creation of the People's Republic of China. The most populous country in the world had become Communist. A look at the political map of the world now showed the Communist part stretching across the globe from Shanghai to Berlin.

Mao's triumph set off a debate in America about "how we lost China" and who was responsible, as if China were an American possession that some people had carelessly let slip from America's grasp. This became a reason to attack people in the State Department and elsewhere who were insufficiently dogmatic in their hostility to Communism, and in some cases it was to cripple or end their careers. The debate was a harbinger of the world that was coming into being, with much of the globe divided into two power blocs, one of them headed by the United States. In this world a country was not to be allowed to slip out of the bloc of which it was a member. Hungary tried to get out of its bloc and failed, Cuba slipped out of the Western bloc and against all the odds it stayed out. America used deception and force to try to get Cuba back in but it could not be as ruthless nor as open as the Soviet Union was in Hungary.

All the foundations of this new world were laid in the years 1946 to 1949. By the end of that period Britain was retreating from its global role and the United States had stepped forward as a new superpower. The American people changed in these three years and accepted a global role for their country. The Communist countries and the West were fixed in opposition to one another. Roosevelt's dream, widely shared, of a world policed by the United Nations led by the big powers was dead and forgotten. Britain remained America's closest ally and even an influential one for many years.

Britain suffered the material consequences of the war longer than most countries. The ruins of bombed buildings were still seen in London after they had been cleared up in most European cities, including some German cities that had been more heavily bombed. Food rationing was not finally abolished until 1954. Britain was slow to accept the decline in its status, and slow to concentrate on the areas that would arrest its continuing decline, such as industrial efficiency and technological excellence. Britons retained a kind of nostalgia for wartime, for the time when Britain had earned the admiration of the world, seen in the occasional evocation of the "Dunkirk spirit," in the prominence given to the war in the teaching of history in schools, and in the frequent identification of Germans with Nazis, sometimes jokingly, sometimes not. For a time Britain seemed like an old soldier fingering his war medals as a compensation for disappointments in civilian life.

NATO developed in ways that could have been foreseen but were not. When the US Senate Foreign Relations Committee was conducting hearings on the treaty, Senator Bourke Hickenlooper of Iowa asked Dean Acheson whether the United States would be expected to send substantial numbers of troops to Europe to contribute to NATO. Acheson responded: "The answer to that question, Senator, is a clear and unequivocal 'No.'"

Acheson was being truthful. At that time the Administration had no intention of sending over a large number of American troops to help defend Europe, and it would not have had Senate support for the idea. No American troops were committed to the NATO command. It was the shock of the North Korean attack on South Korea in June 1950 that led to the creation of a NATO force with a substantial American contribution. Korea was not a political coup, which hitherto had been seen as the danger in Europe, but a military attack across a frontier. Like Korea, Germany was also a divided country with a heavily armed Communist half, and the West Germans were worried. Six months after the North Korean attack, NATO established the Supreme Allied Command Europe, SACEUR, in Paris, with General Eisenhower as Supreme Commander.

As NATO built up its military forces the Western allies had to grasp the nettle of German rearmament. The idea of Germans in uniform still sent shivers down the spine in western Europe. In Germany itself there was opposition from young people who rejected everything their parents' generation had stood for, including militarism. After an attempt to create a European defense force which included a German component had been torpedoed by the French National Assembly, West German armed forces were created. But they were not allowed to operate independently. West Germany would rearm but its armed forces would be locked into the NATO command structure. Although NATO was designed ostensibly for defense against Russia, some quipped that its aim was "to keep Russia out, America in, and Germany down."

As they became more prosperous, European countries set targets for their contributions to NATO which they rarely met. The American nuclear arsenal, on the ground in Europe and elsewhere, became the shield behind which Europe sheltered comfortably, matched by a nuclear arsenal on the other side. European liberals continued to inveigh against America, but this was sniping rather than fullscale attack. Few people really wanted to break the link with the United States. Sometimes this took the form of identifying Washington with reactionary regimes it supported. Sometimes it was establishing a moral equivalence: McCarthyite persecution of liberals with the Soviet labor camps, the bias of some of the American press with the tight state control of media in Communist countries. Sometimes it was simply a sardonic air of superiority. Often a line of Rudyard Kipling came to mind: "making mock o' uniforms which guard you while you sleep."

In January 1949, in his State of the Union address, President Truman announced the creation of another aid program, to underdeveloped countries or what is now called the Third World. The program came to be called Point Four because it was the fourth point he had made in his inaugural address. He introduced it with language similar to that used by General Marshall in his Harvard speech. He said he wanted to help these countries avoid the "drift toward poverty, despair, fear, and the other miseries of mankind which breed unending wars." Much of the rationale, as with the Marshall Plan, was to steer these countries away from the siren voice of Communism. But once again there was also a humanitarian push behind it.

This was to be the Marshall Plan second version. It concentrated more than the Marshall Plan on the transfer of technology. However, it fell far short of expectations. Charles Bohlen reflected on this later:

> One of the reasons the Marshall Plan worked so well was that the sixteen European countries that joined it contained the necessary qualified personnel, skills and institutions. All the United States was doing was injecting a little economic life blood into a system that had stopped functioning. Later, aid plans for underdeveloped countries ran into difficulties because the needed skills had not been developed.

The movement toward European economic integration continued. In 1950, France, Germany, Italy, and the Benelux countries put their coal and steel industries under a common High Authority, a plan conceived by Monnet but launched by the French Prime Minister, Robert Schuman, as the Schuman Plan. This European Coal and Steel Community ensured that France would not see increased German production as a threat. It also, as Monnet said, would make war between France and Germany "not only unthinkable but materially impossible." Britain was invited to join, but true to form it declined. The ECSC morphed into the European Common Market, which morphed into the European Union.

The Marshall Plan was a success, to an unusual degree for an international project. History consists mostly of illustrations of the law of unintended effects. The Marshall Plan achieved just the effect that it set out to achieve. It restored European confidence and the European economies, filling basic needs so that European countries could invest, and it preserved them for democracy and for capitalism.

Between 1948 and 1952, the ERP supplied grants and credits totalling $13,150 million. The largest sum went to the United Kingdom and its dependencies, $3,176 million. France came next with $2,706 million, Italy with $1,474 million, Germany with $1,389 million. Over the Marshall Plan countries as a whole, industrial production in 1947 was 87 percent of the prewar figure. Two years later this figure had risen to 110 percent and in 1951 it was 134 percent. Farm output rose at a similar rate: 86 percent of the prewar figure in 1947–8, reaching 104 percent in 1948–50, and 110 percent in 1950–1. The change was visible in traffic jams on streets where a few years previously one had seen mostly bicycles, and in an expansion of businesses catering to leisure: restaurants, holiday hotels, record stores.

Economic growth did not increase parallel with the amount of aid, for other factors were involved. Britain, which received the largest amount, did not grow as rapidly as France, but it put a lot of its GNP into social services. France started from a lower base, and it was beginning the process of changing, over thirty years, from being a predominantly rural to a predominantly urban nation. West Germany received $514 million and exploded from the direst poverty into prosperity thanks to what the press called "the German economic miracle." But it was using technological and social skills that were already well developed. Italy received more than Germany, and at the end of the Marshall Plan period Italians were still going abroad to look for work. Among the sixteen OEEC countries, Switzerland received no Marshall aid, while Ireland, which had also been neutral in the war and suffered no war damage, received a small amount.

It is worth noting that Japan, which had been damaged by the war as much as Germany, received no Marshall aid, and yet rose to prosperity as rapidly as any of the countries that did, the result of American government and private investment following the outbreak of the Korean War, and of being an extraordinarily organized and disciplined society.

Europe was able to play its part in the global market and contribute to the most rapid economic global growth in history. Increasing prosperity in Europe dulled the edge of class war, and the Soviet Union, suppressing bids for freedom in other East Bloc countries, shed its benign image. In every Western European country Communism receded, and the democratic socialist parties shed most of their socialist ideology. After a few years, capitalism was the only game in town.

The decades that saw a rapid growth in prosperity saw also a withdrawal from empire. Britain, France, Belgium, and Holland gave up most of their overseas possessions and concentrated on domestic concerns. They ceased to maintain large military forces. In this new age, war was not profitable. Germany, like Japan, had gone to war to acquire more living space for its people, and like Japan it prospered in the postwar years without it.

Western European societies had their problems but they enjoyed political stability. Germany, a source of anxiety ever since Bismarck had welded the German states together to create the most powerful nation in Europe, was safely democratic and no danger to anyone. War between European powers was unimaginable.

NATO too was a success in that it achieved its original aim. The Soviet Union never planned to attack western Europe, but NATO, or at any rate the American nuclear guarantee, insured against it. Kennan complained that his policy of containment had become too militarized, and indeed the succeeding years saw a build-up of weapons, including nuclear weapons, on both sides of the dividing line in Europe. The Iron Curtain was respected. The Western powers made no move to help the Hungarians or the Czechs when Soviet tanks crushed their bid for freedom. The rigid stand-off on the ground in Europe mirrored the rigidity of the US–Soviet balance of thermonuclear terror worldwide, in which the bottomless peril created by the megatons left room for maneuver only around the edges of the superpowers' interests.

Eventually, as Kennan had hoped, the Soviet Union, contained within its borders, strained economically by an arms race, defeated in its bid to crush the rebels in Afghanistan, its people exposed more and more to the lifestyle of the wealthier Western democracies, collapsed. Communism died in the Soviet Union and in its eastern European satellites. The USSR, the empire that had been created by the Czars and taken over by the Communists, broke up into its constituent parts.

Joseph Jones in the State Department spoke of Britain having "handed the job of world leadership ... to the United States," and William Clayton, looking at Britain's bankrupt position after the war, talked of America taking from Britain "the reins of world leadership." But "leadership" is often a polite term for dominance. When Britain was a great imperial power and its industry was the powerhouse of the world, it did not do much leading but it did a lot of dominating. America as a superpower has led in the establishment of defense pacts against Communism, and, more ambiguously, in the "war on terror." In some other areas it has failed to exercise leadership where it was called for, such as climate change and international law. But it has done a lot of dominating.

One difference between British and American domination is that the British people were proud of theirs while Americans have been shy about theirs to the point of denial. Most would agree with President George W. Bush when he said in his 2004 State of the Union address, "We have no desire to dominate, no ambitions of empire." For Britons in Victorian times, "The sun never sets on the British Empire" was a proud boast. No American would make a similar boast. But he could. At the last count the United States had thirty-eight major military bases in nine countries, each a little bit of America with its Burger Kings and bowling alleys and movie theaters and swimming pools. But this does not begin to account for the global reach of US military and economic power. American servicemen are stationed at other military facilities around the world, in military assistance programs, landing areas, fuel depots, listening posts. The United States also arms and trains the armed forces of many other countries.

Over the years America has supported governments that suited its purpose and undermined ones that do not. In Europe this has meant supporting democracy against Communism. (Not always. America was friendly to the right-wing military junta that ruled Greece between 1967 and 1974.) Elsewhere, it has often meant supporting dictatorships and sometimes suppressing democracy. Countries rarely exercise power for the benefit of others.

Another difference between American and British dominance is responsibility. Because Britain ruled other countries directly, it had to accept responsibility for them. When troops commanded by a British general killed 900 unarmed Indians in Amritsar, in India, in 1919 the General was court-martialed and the Amritsar massacre became a nail in the coffin of British rule.

The United States does not have colonies in the formal sense and it can distance itself from repression by governments it supports and atrocities by armies it has trained.

Britain forced on its colonies economic policies that suited it, the principal cause of the American Revolution. The United States, without taking colonies, has used its economic power to force other countries to open up their markets, their infrastructure, and even their public utilities to American investment. This is not a new development in American policy; the US has practised it in Central America and the Caribbean since the 1900s. But since World War Two it has been able to do so much more widely. Sometimes American pressure has helped other countries prosper and become more democratic, very often it has not. US economic policies may benefit some but they disadvantage many others. Armies and air forces sometimes use the weapons that America provides and kill people with them. American troops sometimes engage in war and become an occupying army. Often America's high-profile presence alone offends.

Many Americans did not see the impact on other people of the United States as a superpower, so the terrorist attacks on their country came as a surprise. They could only see them as attacks on American democracy, rather than on American power. Yet among many peoples in other parts of the world, these were seen as counter-attacks.

The dominance is cultural as well. America is leading willy-nilly because the world is following. In the days of the British Empire ambitious people around the world aspired to live like British gentlemen; now Americans are the more popular model. In the Indian subcontinent men are abandoning their traditional idea of female beauty and accepting Western ideals from American television. Street gangs in South Africa and Brazil take their names from gangs in American urban ghettos. Once, American students with academic ambitions aimed for a spell at a British university; now a few terms at an American university is a boost to a British academic career. The *New York Review of Books* is required reading in intellectual elites.

Every empire has a mission to accompany its own aggrandizement, something to give to the inhabitants whose lands it uses for its own purposes. For the Spanish Empire this was Catholicism, for the French Empire *la civilisation française*, and for the British Empire Christianity and the rule of law. For the American hegemony, it is democracy and free-market capitalism. When the mission conflicts with the national self-interest it takes second place. But the mission does not disappear. It can be held up as a standard. Jesuit missionaries defended Indians against enslavement in Brazil and Paraguay. Many

British colonial administrators devoted themselves to promoting justice and raising living standards in their areas. Dedicated American aid workers help underdeveloped countries, Congress can on occasion ignore the State Department's approach to foreign policy and speak out for human rights, and a free press can call the Government to account to live up to America's professed standards.*

The example of American democracy, in its promise if not always in its execution, has also spread around the world, as it has been doing from the earliest days of the Republic. The students who challenged the Chinese dictatorship by occupying Tiananmen Square in 1989 carried a model of the Statue of Liberty. When eastern European countries emerged from Communism it was to America that they looked as a model for democratic institutions, and American institutions provided a lot of not entirely disinterested guidance. The United States has changed, but the American dream lives on.

Although the foundations of this new world were completed by the end of 1949, two episodes in the following years underlined and accelerated the changes that were taking place. One was the Iran crisis of 1952–3, the other the Suez crisis in 1956. The first saw America acting out its new role, the second saw Britain finally abandoning its old one.

For most of the twentieth century Iran was dominated by outside powers, with the British, French, and Russians competing for spheres of influence. In 1908 oil was discovered there and the Anglo-Persian Oil Company† got the mining concession. The British Government acquired 51 percent of the shares and a strategic interest in the country and it became the dominant outside power. During World War Two Britain, Russia, and America all stationed troops in Iran to facilitate the movement of supplies through the country from the West to the Soviet Union. In 1941 when the Prime Minister, General Fazlollah Zahedi, was showing pro-German sympathies, British special forces spirited him out of his office at pistol-point. Americans helped run the Finance Ministry and Colonel Norman Schwarzkopf, a West Pointer and former New Jersey police chief, trained the gendarmerie. (His son, General Norman Schwarzkopf, led American forces in the first Gulf war.)

* A hard-edged view is quoted by Thucydides: "Considerations of [right and wrong] have never turned people aside from opportunities of aggrandisement offered by superior strength. Those who really deserve praise are those who, while human enough to enjoy power, nevertheless pay more attention to justice than they are compelled to by their situation" (*The Peloponnesian War*, Book 1, Penguin, London 1954, p. 55).

† It changed its name to the Anglo-Iranian Oil Company when the country changed its name in 1935.

The Anglo-Iranian Oil Company shipped oil from the port of Abadan and took 80 percent of the revenue. The Iranians were dissatisfied. They asked for better terms, closer to the 50 percent that the Arabian-American Oil Company, Aramco, took in Saudi Arabia; they wanted AIOC to appoint more Iranians to management positions; and they wanted better conditions for the company's workers, most of whom were badly paid and lived in Abadan in fetid slums. The company refused to budge. Truman regarded the AIOC as old-fashioned imperialists. He sent Harriman over to mediate but this came to nothing.

In 1951 Mohammed Mosadeq was elected Prime Minister and announced that Iran was nationalizing AIOC, thereby setting off a crisis. Acheson, who like most of the Administration regarded the company's refusal to make concessions as pig-headed, had no sympathy for AIOC. He commented, "Never had so few lost so much so stupidly and so fast." The Shah of Iran was sidelined. Mosadeq, a small, thin man with a hawk nose and limpid eyes, presented a bizarre figure to the West, given to passionate outbursts and sometimes fainting with emotion, but to Iranians this behavior only showed the depth of his commitment to his country.

In the British cabinet some members wanted to use force in Abadan, but Attlee rejected this. He said it would provoke an Iranian backlash, that the United States would be against it, and that it would be contrary to the United Nations charter. Iran expelled all British citizens, and AIOC stopped the flow of oil. As the crisis developed Washington was worried that events were strengthening the Tudeh Party, the Iranian Communist Party, and that the nationalist movement might fall under its sway.

In November 1951 Churchill's Conservative Party won the general election and the new Conservative Government took a more robust attitude toward intervening in other countries. It approved a project by the British secret service to overthrow Mosadeq. But this was no longer the world of 1941 and if the British wanted to remove an Iranian prime minister they would need some help. The Truman Administration would not have anything to do with the idea. But then General Eisenhower replaced Truman in the White House and the attitude in Washington changed. The British sent Christopher Woodhouse, who divided his time between Middle East scholarship and intelligence work, to Washington with the SIS plan. He saw Secretary of State John Foster Dulles and Allen Dulles, the Director of the CIA, and received a sympathetic response. He told them that Mosadeq was too closely tied to the Tudeh Party and would not be able to resist a Tudeh coup. As he admitted later, "I decided to emphasize the Communist threat to Iran rather than the need to recover the oil industry."

Allen Dulles was ready to turn his CIA loose on the task of replacing a foreign government, going far beyond its original mandate. To organize the coup he chose Kermit Roosevelt, grandson of Theodore, a CIA operator in the Middle East who knew the area well and was a personal acquaintance of the Shah.

The details of the coup are cloak-and-dagger stuff with a lot of deception. The SIS had been thrown out of Iran along with other British citizens, but it had had Iranians on its payroll and it turned these over to the CIA. Roosevelt established himself in the country under an alias and coopted some military men. As Mosadeq's successor he chose General Fazlollah Zahedi, the man the British had removed from office during the war because of his pro-German sympathies. Schwarzkopf was brought back to help persuade the Shah. The Shah wanted proof from the top that the British and American governments would back him, and this was supplied. President Eisenhower inserted an agreed phrase into a speech he was making in San Francisco, and the BBC World Service announcer said on a prearranged date, not "It is midnight" but "It is exactly midnight." The SIS played a part outside Iran, among other things bringing the Shah's sister onside.

The plotters set out to destabilize the country, bribing some members of the Majlis, the Iranian parliament, and organizing attacks on the religious establishment supposedly carried out by the Tudeh Party, to stir up anti-Tudeh feeling. They bribed newspapers to carry anti-Mosadeq articles. They dispatched messages to religious leaders supposedly from Mosadeq supporters warning that they would be killed if they did not back Mosadeq, stirring up resentment against him. Roosevelt and his Iranian agents sent anti-Shah mobs out on the streets looting and burning. Then, when these had aroused fear and anger, they sent out pro-Shah mobs, with Roosevelt handing out money in the bazaars. The plot almost failed. The Shah announced that he was arresting Mosadeq, only for Mosadeq to escape. The Shah fled to Rome, and some of the coup officers were arrested. Roosevelt, improvising continually, regained control of the situation and the streets, the Shah was reinstated, and Mosadeq arrested. Three hundred people were killed in the street fighting.

The Iranian oil industry went back into private hands, but not to the Anglo-Iranian Oil Company. America had organized the coup and wanted some of the fruits. A new oil company was set up in which American oil companies had 40 percent of the shares.

For Allen Dulles the coup was a success. It showed what his CIA could do. James Jesus Angleton, the head of CIA counter-intelligence, said later in a BBC television program, "It was our first pair of long pants." This ushered in a new era in which the United States was both willing and able to use the CIA to replace a foreign government with one that suited American policies.

Roosevelt said the coup succeeded because the army and the majority of people were on their side. He told Dulles, "If we, the CIA, are ever going to try something like this again we must be absolutely sure that the people and the army want what we want." Dulles told him that the CIA were planning to overthrow the left-wing government elected in Guatemala, which had nationalized the United Fruit Company, and offered him the job of organizing this. Roosevelt said that neither of those conditions applied there and turned down the job. It is not clear whether his objection was tactical or moral. If it was moral he would have had a strong case. The military government the CIA installed in Guatemala was not wanted by the people, and it massacred some 200,000 of them over the next two decades.

The Shah continued his modernization program but did not go as far as his American backers expected nor in the direction that they wanted. He ruled autocratically with the help of Savak, his secret police known principally for their tortures. Despite the Shah's method of ruling and the American disappointment, successive administrations hailed him as a friend and the American military trained his army officers. Woodhouse, who played a part in the coup, wrote later: "What we did not foresee was that the Shah would gather new strength and use it so capriciously and tyrannically, nor that the U.S. Government and the Foreign Office would fail so abjectly to keep him on a reasonable course." Evidently, even such sophisticated operators as Woodhouse himself and Kermit Roosevelt overestimated the degree to which Western-style democracy could be exported to a different culture, a mistake other Americans were to make in the Middle East.

When the Shah was overthrown in 1979, it was not by democrats but by Islamists. The new Iranian leader, the Ayatollah Khomeini, drawing lessons from the past, said, "We are not liberals like Mosadeq and Allende, who the CIA can just snuff out." The new Iranian leadership denounced America as "the great Satan" (the Bush Administration returned the compliment using the same quasi-religious language, labeling Iran part of the axis of evil). Forced into exile, the Shah was welcomed in the United States by President Carter. Iranians guessed that another American-backed coup to reinstate the Shah might be in the offing, so radical students seized the US Embassy and held the fifty-two members of staff hostage for fourteen months.

The coup that overthrew Mosadeq is largely forgotten in America and Britain, but it is remembered in Iran, and indeed all over the Middle East, and the memory invites skepticism about American statements that it wants to promote democracy in the area. Years later, giving a speech at Cairo University in 2005, Secretary of State Condoleeza Rice recognized America's history of support for tyrants in the Middle East and offered a promise of change. "For sixty years," she said, "my country, the United States, pursued stability at the expense of democracy in this region, and we achieved neither." She added, "Now, we are taking a different course. We are supporting the democratic aspirations of all people."

The Suez crisis in 1956 was a watershed in British history. It finally put paid to any lingering idea that Britain was a great imperial power, and created a deep division in the country. This happened because the British Government embarked on a project that was both mendacious and foolish.

For the first half of the twentieth century Egypt was nominally independent but it was under British domination until the early 1950s, when Britain withdrew its troops. Britain's principal interest there was the Suez Canal, owned by an Anglo-French company in which the British Government held shares. When Britain had an empire in Asia the canal was a vital link and a symbol of Britain's imperial reach.

In 1952 a group of Egyptian army officers overthrew King Farouk, a short, plump, comical-looking figure known more for his sybaritic lifestyle than for dedication to good government. Their leader, although he remained in the background at first, was Colonel Gamel Abdel Nasser. Nasser was a pan-Arabist, who wanted to unite the Arab world. He became an immensely popular figure, who gave Egyptians a sense of national pride after being dominated by foreigners for centuries (or millennia if one goes back to the ethnically Greek Ptolemies). Two years later Britain withdrew its troops from the Suez Canal Zone.

Britain at that time was still the dominant power in the Middle East. British officers commanded the Jordanian Army, Britain ruled by proxy the oil sheikhdoms that are now the Gulf states, and it had bases in Iraq. Nasser's Voice of the Arabs radio challenged British influence everywhere. In February 1956 Jordan's King Hussein, yielding to nationalist pressure exacerbated by Nasser's propaganda, expelled his Army's British officers.

Nasser had a scheme to dam the River Nile at Aswan, which would provide electric power and irrigate large areas, opening them up to agriculture. America was going to finance the project under World Bank supervision. Then Nasser, having had his request to buy arms from Britain and America turned down, announced a deal to buy weapons from Russia. The US Government withdrew its offer to finance the Aswan dam.

Mohammed Heykal, a newspaper editor and confidant of Nasser, had an idea. The Suez Canal Company was getting $100 million a year in revenues from shipping and paying only $3 million in tax. Why not, he suggested to Nasser, make the Suez Canal Company pay more and use the money to finance the dam? Why not make it pay 50 percent of its revenues?

Nasser had a better idea. "Why fifty-fifty?" he replied. "Why not one hundred percent?"

On July 26, a week after the American withdrawal of the finance offer, Nasser announced that he was nationalizing the Suez Canal Company. As he spoke Egyptian troops took over the company's offices. The Suez Canal was a vital international waterway and Nasser's announcement aroused anxiety around the world.

Nowhere was the shock greater than in Britain, which, like the rest of Europe, was dependent on oil and other materials coming from the Persian Gulf through the canal. Newspapers talked of a "stranglehold" on Britain. The Government said the canal must be put under international control. With British rule of the Indian subcontinent ended, it was no longer a lifeline of empire, but for many British people the Suez Canal had a symbolic as well as a strategic significance. The Colonial Secretary, Alan Lennox-Boyd, wrote in a memo to the cabinet: "I am firmly convinced that if Nasser wins, or even appears to win, we might as well as a government (and indeed as a country) go out of business." This was the voice of a man who had lived his whole life in a Britain that was at the head of a great empire and could not imagine any other kind of Britain.

The Prime Minister, Anthony Eden, had resigned as Foreign Secretary in 1938 and come out in opposition to Chamberlain's appeasement policy, and he compared Nasser to Hitler and Mussolini and characterized talk of compromise as appeasement. Eden had an image as a sophisticated, debonair figure, but in private he was given to outbursts of rage. These were exacerbated by a bile problem, which was being treated by injections with only limited effect. When the Minister of State at the Foreign Office, Sir Anthony Nutting, composed a memo about neutralizing Nasser's influence, Eden telephoned him and shouted, "What's all this nonsense about isolating Nasser or neutralizing him? I want him destroyed! Can't you understand?"

There were diplomatic moves with the United States playing a role. Egypt kept the canal traffic moving. The British Government called up military reserves and began moving ships to Malta and Cyprus. It received many warnings against military action. The Chiefs of Staff said that if Britain invaded Egypt it must be ready to reoccupy the canal zone, force a change of government, and support the new one. Middle East ambassadors warned against military action. The US Government made clear its opposition. Nonetheless Eden continued with his plans, keeping everyone except the cabinet and service chiefs in the dark.

Nasser made other enemies: France, because he was backing his fellow-Arabs in Algeria who were fighting for independence from France, and Israel, because infiltrators were staging terrorist attacks across the Egyptian frontier into Israel. France was on good terms with Israel and was supplying it with weapons.

The crisis atmosphere continued through the summer and autumn and then other events claimed the world's attention. In Hungary the Prime Minister Imre Nagy announced radical reforms which would herald the end of Communist dictatorship and asked Russia to withdraw its troops from the country. In America the Presidential election was under way with General Eisenhower running for a second term against Adlai Stevenson.

On October 29 Israeli forces attacked in the Sinai desert. The next day Britain and France sent identical notes to Egypt and Israel, asking them to withdraw their forces ten miles from the canal. They said that the war represented a danger to shipping in the canal, and in order to safeguard it British and French forces would temporarily occupy key positions on the canal. If Israel and Egypt did not agree within twelve hours, British and French forces would intervene "in whatever strength necessary to secure compliance."

This was transparently an excuse to seize the canal. There was uproar in Parliament mingled with incredulity. The Labour Party came out in angry opposition. Some pointed out that withdrawing ten miles from the canal would still leave the Israelis deep inside Egyptian territory. The American Administration was furious as it had not been consulted. Secretary of State John Foster Dulles told a group of reporters that Britain had forced the United States to declare itself for or against Western colonialism. He told the chargé d'affaires at the British Embassy, "We are facing the destruction of trust in each other."

When the twelve-hour deadline passed, the RAF bombed Egyptian airfields to immobilize the Egyptian Air Force, and two days later British and French paratroopers landed in Port Said and Ismalia, at the two ends of the Suez Canal Zone. They met fierce opposition. The Israelis accepted a UN request for a ceasefire, which removed the pretext for further Anglo-French action, but the British carried out a sea landing anyway. The UN General Assembly condemned the attack with only five abstentions, America and the Soviet Union for once voting together.

On October 30, the day of the invasion, Russia agreed to pull Soviet troops out of Hungary and they began to withdraw. Three days later the Russians arrested the Hungarian general who had gone to parley and sent Soviet forces back into Hungary. Front pages around the world showed pictures of Soviet tanks in the streets of Budapest crushing Hungary's bid for freedom in street battles, and also the fighting in Port Said. President Eisenhower was incensed by this diversion of attention from the Soviet aggression in Hungary. Some even said that the Anglo-French assault, by setting an example of Western aggression, had enabled the Soviet Union to act as it did.

In Britain the Government's opponents suspected what seemed obvious: that Britain, France, and Israel had planned the whole thing together: the Israeli attack and the Anglo-French ultimatum that followed. Eden denied this. In fact the three countries had colluded. The Israeli attack and the Anglo-French intervention had been planned at a secret meeting between the British and French foreign ministers and the Israeli Prime Minister, David Ben-Gurion, in Sèvres, in France. French aircraft were even providing air cover for Israel, some of them operating secretly out of Israeli airfields. This was disclosed in the following years by French and Israeli sources.

The invasion created angry divisions among the British public. Emotions ran high. Families who in normal times did not even talk about politics were split by violent quarrels on the issue. Phrases like "traitor" and "stab in the back" were thrown around. They were hurled at Hugh Gaitskell, the Labour Party leader, because he denounced the invasion while British troops were going into battle.

This was a clash between two ideas of what Britain stood for. Some Britons cheered. The British lion was roaring again. Britain was showing that it would not be pushed around by some Arab dictator, and that it did not have to ask America's permission to assert itself. Others saw this as illegal aggression, an outburst of chauvinist rage based on a lie. A mass rally to protest against the war filled Trafalgar Square in London, the biggest upsurge of feeling since prewar days. Demonstrators carried banners saying "Law Not War" and "Eden Must Go." A new generation was finding its voice, people who were prouder of the National Health Service than of the British Empire.

One factor in the enthusiasm among many British people for the attack on Egypt which was rarely acknowledged was a racist hostility, particularly among working-class men, toward Arabs and especially Egyptians. Millions of British soldiers had either been stationed in or had passed through the Middle East during the war, and they came back with a contempt for Egyptians - "wogs" or "gyppos" - whom they tended to regard as bazaar cheats and pimps. This attitude was not limited to the working class. I remember a senior editor at Reuters news agency who had worked in the Middle East saying when the military officers overthrew King Farouk: "It looks as if Neguib will be taking over and that might just work out, because Neguib is a Sudanese. An Arab could no more govern a country than my dog could."

There is only one reference to this factor in print that I have seen, and it came, perhaps understandably, from an Arab scholar long resident in England, A. H. Hourani. In a monograph on the Suez crisis published by St Antony's College, Oxford he wrote: "The contempt which power breeds has been directed above all on to the Egyptians, just as in France it has been directed on to the Algerians. It is doubtful whether an attack on any other people in the world would have aroused as much enthusiasm as an attack on the Egyptians."

The Anglo-French intervention was supposedly designed to keep the canal open, but the Egyptians sank ships at key points in the canal to block shipping. One immediate consequence was an oil shortage in Europe and gasoline rationing. America and Venezuela sent oil across the Atlantic to make up for the oil from the Persian Gulf that could not pass through the Suez Canal. In those days America was a net exporter of oil. Tensions over the Middle East were raised higher when the Soviet Union inserted itself into the crisis. The Soviet premier, Nikolai Bulganin, made a veiled threat of nuclear attack on Britain and France in response to their assault on Egypt, and reaped benefits in terms of goodwill in the Arab world.

It is hard to see how the British Government could have sustained its position for long in the face of such strong opposition at home and abroad, but what got it out of Egypt was a financial crisis. When the canal was nationalized there was a run on sterling, and this became more serious when the canal was closed. The Chancellor of the Exchequer, Harold Macmillan, said that Britain would have to turn to Washington and the International Monetary Fund. The United States demanded that the British pull out before it would help. Britain and France duly withdrew, to be replaced by a UN force that patrolled the Sinai desert between Israeli and Egyptian forces for the next nine years.

The attack on Egypt had been intended to free the canal and bring down Nasser. It closed the canal, enhanced Nasser's prestige, for he was hailed as the man who had driven back an Anglo-French invasion, boosted Russia's status in the Arab world, reduced British influence, and showed the British and French governments to have acted in bad faith.

In Britain some Conservatives were angry with the United States and with their Government for giving in to it, some of them the same ones who had wanted to refuse the 1946 US loan. Julian Amery, the leader of a right-wing imperialist group in the Conservative Party, said in Parliament, "The Americans want to take our place in the Middle East and they want to take the place of France in North Africa. They want the economic assets, they want to run the show." This was another manifestation of the anti-Americanism on the right, resentful of Britain's loss of power.

With British influence in the Middle East severely damaged, President Eisenhower proclaimed what became known as the Eisenhower Doctrine. In a speech to Congress two months after the Anglo-French withdrawal from Suez, he asked Congress to authorize the use of military force if necessary to defend Middle East countries from Communism, and promised economic and military help. Congress obliged. Mohammed Heykal wrote later: "The business of easing Britain out of the Middle East and easing America in was conducted with almost indecent haste."

Never again would Britain try to act as a great imperial power. Never again would it undertake a major international venture alone. Four months after the Suez debacle Anthony Eden, by now a sick man, resigned, and was succeeded by Harold Macmillan. Macmillan set out to repair the bridges to Washington that Eden had wrecked. He had the advantage of having worked with Eisenhower during the war. He sought a new role for Britain. He dismantled the African empire, giving independence to Britain's African colonies, and applied for entry into what was then the European Common Market. President de Gaulle vetoed British entry. Membership would have to wait until 1973.

Later Eden wrote that the Suez adventure "has not so much changed our fortunes as revealed realities." This was true. The episode revealed for even the most short-sighted the shift in global power that was signaled in those British notes on Greece and Turkey delivered to the State Department on a wintry day in February 1947.

All Europe was part of this. For six centuries Europe had been the dynamic center of world events, the principal source of the changes that had swept across the world, centuries which saw the Reformation, the Enlightenment, the Industrial Revolution, the spread of empire. Now the center had moved across the Atlantic.

Some might take a historically deterministic view. They might say that this change in the world was inevitable, whatever happened during the four years after the war. They would say that the trend of history was moving in that direction. Britain had been declining in economic power since the 1900s; a spirit of revolt was abroad among colonial peoples and the European empires were doomed. They would say America was the most powerful country in the world and was bound to use its power globally, that power was going to pass across the Atlantic anyway, that this was all going to happen some time and somehow.

Perhaps. But this was when it did happen and this is how it happened.

NOTES

Abbreviations

FRUS: Foreign Relations of the United States, series published by the US State Department, Washington DC
HSTL: Harry S. Truman Library, Independence, MO
NA: UK National Archives, London

Chapter One: After Victory

4 "called into existence the New World;" speech by George Canning in 1826. He was warning France against attempting to conquer the South American countires that had recently gained independence from Spain.
5 Millicent King, raising two children; Forster, 83
5 The American writer Edmund Wilson; Wilson, 216
7 "I hear you've had;" Dalton, *Diary*, 383
7 The young Barbara Castle; Howard, 169
8 "The first sensation;" Dalton, *High Tide*, 3
8 When he visited America; Jack Jones, 188
9 The young Princess Elizabeth; Gaitskell, entry April 23, 1948
10 One returning serviceman recalled; Kynaston, 112
10 "The French called;" Waugh, entry November 23, 1946
12 "To the young veterans;" Manchester, 419
13 Here is the recollection; Goulden, 48
14 Attlee letter to Truman; Gowing, 78
15 He wrote to his parents; Smith, 341
15 Meyer wrote in his diary; Meyer, 33
16 John J. McCloy, the US Assistant Secretary; Truman, 102
18 Paul-Henri Spaak on law-breaking; Mayne, *Postwar*, 27
18 German hairdressing salon; *New Statesman*, March 4, 1947
18 "I must confess that my exultation;" Clay, 21
20 Some American officials were even unwilling; Ibid., 122
20 Attlee asked Truman; Mayne, *Postwar*, 110.
21 John Bross saw red flags; Pisani, 181
21 Edmund Wilson in Rome; Wilson, 254
22 Bernard Braden recollection; Braden, 23

22 Roosevelt, "Please don't ask me;" Dallek, 476
23 Years later General Marshall recalled; Speech to National Preparedness Conference, November 1950, quoted in Goulden, 35
23 "It was a great shock;" Harris, *Prime Minister*, 129
24 "the Missouri courthouse calibre;" NA, FO371, 56706
24 "Mebbe so, Lord Keynes;" Gardner, 201
25 John Kenneth Galbraith called it; Galbraith, 158
26 The *Economist* comment; issue of December 15, 1945

Chapter Two: Communism and Coca-Cola

28 "It was to disturb me;" Acheson, *Creation*, 164
28 Meeting on the British atomic bomb; Gowing, 183; Hennessy, 268
29 Attlee told an interviewer; Harris, *Prime Minister*, 288
29 "Any suggestion that valuables;" Gowing, 243
30 "The whole question of our relations;" Ibid., 265
30 "You don't keep a dog;" Harris, *Prime Minister*, 268
31 Bevin exchange with Chaim Weizmann; Bullock, 436
32 "I am anxious to promote;" NA, FO800/475, ME445/1
32 Bevin said to Dalton; Dalton, *Diary*, entry October 15, 1948
32 Attlee wrote in a memo; NA, FO371/30, R2443
32 "If we evacuate the area;" NA, FO800/468, GRE46/40
33 A Foreign Office memo warned; NA, FO371/50, R2969
34 Tom Driberg on civil war; Sissons and French, 312
34 "I am beginning to wonder;" NA, FO800/425 ME46/22
35 "The Americans must realize;" NA, FO371, ME47/15
35 Truman to diplomats; Hamby, 493
37 "The attempt of Lenin;" Ibid., 393
39 Halifax complained in a cable; NA, FO371, AN3853/35/45
39 Details of propaganda effort against Russia; Aldrich, 180
41 "Did I do right?" Grose, 73
43 Kennan on the reception of the long telegram; Kennan, 295
44 Harry Hopkins on the Russians; quoted by Robert Sherwood, *Roosevelt and Hopkins. An Intimate History*, Harper Brothers, New York 1948, p. 992
44 Thompson recollection of 1945 election; E. P. Thompson, 224
45 Attlee to Sulzberger; Sulzberger, 212
45 "British socialism is represented;" *New Statesman*, September 28, 1948
46 American academics warned against becoming Anglophile; Winks, 266
46 Michael Young on Hollywood films; Weight, 178
46 "In a Europe that is tired;" *Sight and Sound*, Winter 1948
47 Sir Michael Balcon on British films; Weight, 180
50 "That was the end of Morgenthauism;" F. Taylor Ostrander in an interview with the author

54 Roosevelt told Halifax; NA, FO371, AN385/35/45
54 Acheson message on Indochina; Donovan, 270

Chapter Three: Like a Young Man Pushed Out on His Own

57 *World Factbook*, published annually by the CIA in Washington DC
58 Miners' attitude to Poles; NA, PREM8/729
59 J. L. Hodson wrote in his diary; 'Fuel Crisis 1947', a Mass Observation report in MO files, University of Sussex, p. 20
60 Shinwell memo to Attlee; Robertson, 47
60 "This is a complete thunderclap;" Dalton, *Diary*, 350
60 The journalist Anne Scott-James; *Picture Post*, April 19, 1947, quoted in Robertson, 168
60 Maggie Joy Blunt wrote; Garfield, 374
60 Edie Rutherford wrote; Ibid., 362
61 Dalton to Attlee; Dalton, *High Tide*, 39
61 Attlee memo on Greece; NA, FO371/50, R2443
61 "a very poor investment;" NA, PREM8/528
62 Cabinet committee meeting; Dalton, *Diary*, entry February 19, 1947
62 Message to Washington on Greece and Turkey; NA, FO271/07031, R1900/50/919
63 "He is the great one;" Hamby, 388
63 Kindleberger on Marshall; Kindleberger, 109
63 "I shall expect of you;" Acheson, *Creation*, 216
63 "You can't operate and plan;" Pogue, *Interviews*, 562
64 "They were shockers;" Acheson, *Creation*, 217
64 "The defeat of disintegration"; Best, 61
65 "We're going to do it;" Acheson, *Creation*, 218; Henderson oral interview, HSTL
66 Acheson lunch with Louis Fisher; Isaacson and Thomas, 393
66 "It didn't really strike home;" Acheson oral interview, HSTL
67 Alert Athenian politicians; Woodhouse, *Apple*, 77
67 The CIA's Miles Copeland; Copeland, 32
67 Truman meeting with congressional leaders; Acheson, *Creation*, 219; Pogue, *Statesman*, 199
68 Changes in Truman text; Joseph M. Jones, 148 *et seq.*; Pogue, *Statesman*, 221
69 George Elsey complained; Bledsoe Bonds, 155
69 Kennan view; Joseph M. Jones, 155
69 Marshall's view; Bohlen, 261
69 *New York Times* editorial, March 14, 1947
70 Gladwyn Jebb view; NA, FO371/675882
70 Dalton listened to this; Dalton, *High Tide*, 207–9
72 Dalton–Acheson exchange on costs; NA, PREM528
72 Senator Case to Truman; Hartman, 64
73 Advice to Greece; Henderson oral interview, HSTL
77 From Paris Sam White reported; *Evening Standard*, London, June 23, 1947

Chapter Four: A Speech at Harvard

81 Bevin advancing on Molotov; Bohlen, 212
82 Bevin and Acheson arm in arm; Acheson, *Creation*, 301
82 Bidault drunk; Edward Mason oral interview, HSTL; also personal information
83 Stalin had aged; Bohlen, 202
83 Malraux was giving correspondents; Kindleberger, 26
83 Lost Soviet note; Williams, 239
86 "The situation must be faced;" Donovan, 287
86 Vandenberg went to Truman; Joseph M. Jones, 238
87 Clayton's two memos; Joseph M. Jones, 246; Garwood, 100 *et seq.*
88 Kennan started weeping; Isaacson and Thomas, 405
88 Policy Planning Staff document; FRUS *1947*, III, 397–405
89 Acheson lunch with correspondents; Miall oral interview, HSTL; Acheson, *Creation*, 228
91 "Bill, we know what he said;" Acheson, *Sketches*, 16
93 like "watching a child bleed to death;" Dalton, *High Tide*, 7
93 "If Britain does not receive;" FRUS *1947*, III, 337
94 "These reserves must only be;" NA, PREM8/489
94 The cabinet secretary found Dalton; Pimlott, 228
94 "I saw spectres;" Dalton, *High Tide*, 254
95 Robert Lovett said that the British Government; Forrestal, entry September 10, 1947
95 Lewis Strauss was concerned about Britain; Lilienthal, 385
95 A group composed of representatives; Hennessy, 299
96 J. B. Priestley broadcast; Quoted in Garfield, 409
97 Clayton meetings with British ministers; FRUS *1947*, III, 268–72
97 Bevin leaned over to Piers Dixon; Bullock, 357
100 Joseph Jones account; Joseph M. Jones, 130
100 Dean Acheson later quoted approvingly; Acheson, *Creation*, 220

Chapter Five: Inventing Europe

104 General Marshall wrote; FRUS *1947*, V, 273
104 Kennan view of negotiations; Ibid., III, 397
104 Sir Eric Roll and Greeks; Behrman, 98
105 As was stated by a report to the US Administration; Clark Clifford papers, HSTL
105 Lovett cabled Clayton; Bledsoe Bonds, 54
106 They were "stacked committees;" Henderson oral interview, HSTL
006 As a member of Will Clayton's staff recalled; Bledsoe Bonds, 46
107 Gaitskell diary note on John Taber; Gaitskell, entry October 22, 1947
107 Herter Committee report; Van der Beugel, 92
108 As *Time* magazine reported admiringly; Hopkins, 122

108 "bottom of the barrel;" FRUS *1947*, III, 472
109 Lovett wrote to Caffery; Carew, 45
110 "Can you imagine its chances?" Donovan, 187
110 State/Army/Navy Committee report; Ibid., 188
110 Wilson, Roosevelt and Acheson quotes from Williams, 58, 162, 203
111 Hoffman address to Foreign Trade Convention; Pisani, 81
112 Lincoln Gordon, writing about that time; "Looking Back on the Marshall Plan," *Journal of International Affairs*, issue 41, 1948
113 One man working through the night; Kindleberger, 117
113 "My goodness, they went back home;" Pogue, *Interviews*, 527
115 Richard Strout in the *New Statesman*, January 31, 1948
115 Marshall and politicians; Isaacson and Thomas, 246
115 Nixon and his constituents; Ambrose, *Nixon*, 158
116 Truman letter to wife, dated September 30, 1947; Original in HSTL
117 Lovett exhausted; Lilienthal, 267
117 Clay telegram; Bledsoe Bonds, 163
118 Georges Bidault told Bruce; FRUS 1947, III, 617
119 Nancy Mitford letter; Mitford, 92
121 As Charles Kindleberger said later; Kindleberger, 110
121 "Depending on which end;" Acheson, *Creation*, 132
121 "I have probably made;" Ibid., 233
122 British cabinet paper; NA, CAB123/13, June 25, 1948
123 Rome Embassy dispatch; Pisani, 107
124 US funding and Italian elections; Pisani, Grose, others
127 Quote from Trilling novel; Lionel Trilling,*The Middle of the Journey*, Viking Press, New York 1947, 123
127 The young partisan Lola Ribar; Quoted in Vladimir Dedijer, *Tito*, Simon & Schuster, New York 1954
128 The writer Ignazio Silone; *The God That Failed*, ed. Arthur Koestler Hamish Hamilton, London 1950, 206
129 Jewish groups bombarded the Administration; Hamby, 407–9
129 Forrestal told Truman; Ibid., 411
130 Marshall–Truman exchange; Isaacson and Thomas, 452; Donovan, 380

Chapter Six: America to the Rescue

131 As F. Taylor Ostrander wrote; Ostrander, 31
132 "The battle is between;" Hoffman, 16
132 Nitze came over; Behrman, 180
132 "Richard Bissell, a New Dealish college professor;" Quoted in Pelling, 120
132 "The ECA cannot understand;" NA, FO371/7765
133 "pandemonium broke loose;" van der Bengel, 151
134 Hubert Havlik recalled; Havlik oral interview, HSTL

135 "The French are tired;" Flanner, 182
137 Press dubbed farms "White collectives"; Author's interview with Ostrander
137 ECA encouraged emigration; Pisani, 190
137 Monnet wrote to Prime Minister; Hacker, 60
138 Engineering company became bankrupt, fascist ECA official; Kipping and Bjarnar, 202
139 Howard Hunt and ECA; Behrman, 186
139 *Chicago Tribune* editorial, January 28, 1949
139 Bevin cabled Marshall; FRUS *1948*, III, 411
140 ECA propaganda effort; Pisani, 92; Behrman, 237 *et seq*.
140 "American propaganda arouses;" Pisani, 92
141 Hoffman said European workers; Hoffman, 101
142 "dark, dingy factories;" Kuisel, 181
142 Reports of British productivity delegations are in the TUC archives, Metropolitan University of London
143 (London) *Times* correspondent's report; *The Times*, January 24, 1948
143 *St Louis Post-Dispatch*, March 16, 1947; *Life* magazine, March 17, 1949; Quoted in van der Beugel, 101
143 George Washington wrote; *The Writings of George Washington* ed. W. C. Ford, vol. IX, p. 2,847. Quoted in van der Beugel, 101
143 Memorandum on European integration; Kindleberger, Appendix
145 Duff Cooper diary entry, August 10, 1947
145 BBC radio program report; Radio 4, August 8, 2006
146 Marshall message to Douglas; FRUS *1948*, III, 447
146 Kennan dispatch on Britain; FRUS *1949*, I, 52
146 "If you open that Pandora's box;" Strang, 250
148 "give them this talking shop;" Bullock, 412
148 Bevin memo to Marshall; FRUS *1948*, III, 15
149-50 Bevin–Bidault conversation on train; NA, FO371/273, 2259
150-51 Churchill view; FRUS *1948*, III, 90

Chapter Seven: Confrontation

155 Marshall cabled Douglas; FRUS *1948*, II, 32
155 Truman determined West should stay in Berlin; Tusa and Tusa, 114
157 "I know you Americans want;" Bohlen, 282
157 "trying to stop the Americans;" Dalton, *High Tide*, 440
157 David Bruce cable; FRUS *1948*, II, 658
157 "Weren't there ever any Nazis?" *New Statesman*, October 9, 1948
158 Truman wrote in his diary; Hamby, 445
158 The Policy Planning Staff produced an assessment; FRUS *1948*, III, 185
158 Magazine articles on possibility of war; *Saturday Evening Post*, November 14, 1948; *Newsweek*, May 17, 1948; *Time*, October 19, 1947

158 "If the Communists seized;" Forrestal, September 26, 1947
158 Joint Chiefs of Staff memo; FRUS *1948*, II, 290
159 Truman told David Lilienthal; Lilienthal, 474
159 "The President said he prayed;" Forrestal, September 28, 1947
159 "There was not a sufficient;" Meyer, 54
161 Planning by two air force commanders; Campbell, 121; Hopkins, 88
161 Acheson–Franks confidential talks; Acheson, *Creation*, 323
161 Acheson on US–UK relationship; Brinkley, 32
161 He ordered all copies burned; Acheson, *Creation*, 388
162 Lord Inverchapel wrote; NA, FO371/68113
162 State Department policy on UK; FRUS *1948*, III, 1092
163 Bevin wrote to Marshall; Ibid., 1009
163-4 Lewis Douglas dispatch; Ibid., 1113
166 Thomas Jefferson quote on Bonaparte; Letter to Thomas Leiper, January 1, 1814
166 Marshall's top-secret message; Henderson, 12
167 Paper by Hickerson; Louis and Bull, 101
167 Lovett and Vandenberg concoct Resolution; Isaacson and Thomas, 450
168 Francis Wilcox said privately; Ibid.
168 Charles Bohlen wrote; Bohlen, 437
169 Truman's sister Mary Jane; Hamby, 433

Chapter Eight: Committed and Entangled

173 Kennan paper; FRUS *1948*, III, 285
174 British cabinet discussed Portugal; NA, CAB128/13, November 4, 1948
177 Acheson explained what they; Acheson, *Creation*, 308
177 Bevin–Vishinsky exchanges; Ibid., 298
179 "to create circumstances;" Hoopes and Brinkley, 312
179 "stop short of the physical;" Grose, 103
179 Bissell on the OPC; Pisani, 172
181 Forrestal's suicide; Hoopes and Brinkley, 464
180-1 Details of covert anti-Soviet warfare; Grose; Smith
182 Meyer's career in CIA; Meyer; Smith; Hersh
184 Talks on nuclear weapons cooperation; Acheson, *Creation*, 314–21; Lilienthal, 547–52
186 Hickenlooper–Acheson exchange; Acheson, *Creation*, 285
187 "making mock o' uniforms;" From Kipling's poem about "Tommy" the much put-upon common soldier Tommy Atkins
187 Bohlen on Point Four aid; Bohlen, 266
188 Monnet "not only unthinkable;" BBC radio program, Radio 4, August 8, 2006
193 "I decided to emphasize;" Woodhouse, *Something Ventured*, 117
194 Details of the Iranian coup; Kinzer; Roosevelt; Woodhouse
195 "If we, the CIA;" Roosevelt, 210

195 "We are not liberals;" Kinzer, 288
197 Heykal–Nasser exchange; Heykal, *Lion's Tail*, 12
197 "What's all this nonsense;" Nutting, 34
200 Hourani passage is from *The Middle East Crisis of 1956*, St Antony's Papers no. 4, 1968
201 Mohammed Heykal wrote; Heykal, *Lion's Tail*, 180
201 Eden wrote; Quoted in Weight, 272

BIBLIOGRAPHY

Acheson, Dean, *Present at the Creation*, Hamish Hamilton, London 1970

Acheson, Dean, *Sketches from Life*, Greenwood Press, Westport, CT 1974

Aldrich, Richard J., *The Hidden Hand. Britain, America and Cold War Secret Intelligence*, John Murray, London 2001

Ambrose, Stephen, *Rise to Globalism. American Foreign Policy Since 1938*, Allen Lane, Penguin Press, London, 1971

Ambrose, Stephen, *Nixon. The Education of a Politician 1913–1962*, Simon & Schuster, New York 1987

Barker, Dudley, *Harvest Home. The Story of the Great Floods of 1947*, Providence Press, London 1985

Barnett, Correlli, *The Lost Victory*, Macmillan, London 1995

Behrman, Greg, *The Most Noble Adventure. The Marshall Plan and the Time When America Helped Save Europe*, Free Press, New York 2007

Beloff, Nora, *Transit of Britain*, Collins, London 1973

Bissell, Richard, *Reflections of a Cold Warrior. From Yalta to the Bay of Pigs*, Yale University Press, New Haven 1996

Bledsoe Bonds, John, *Bipartisan Strategy. Selling the Marshall Plan*, Praeger, Westport, CT 2000

Bohlen, Charles, *Witness to History*, W. W. Norton, New York 1973

Braden, Bernard, *The Kindness of Strangers*, Hodder & Stoughton, London 1997

Brinkley, Douglas, *Dean Acheson and the Making of U.S. Foreign Policy*, Macmillan, London 1993

Bullock, Alan, *Ernest Bevin*, Politico's, London 2002

Burnham, James, *The Managerial Revolution*, John Day, New York 1941

Burnham, James, *The Struggle for the World*, Jonathan Cape, London 1947

Campbell, Duncan, *The Unsinkable Aircraft Carrier*, Michael Joseph, London 1984

Carabott, Philip and Thanasis D. Sifkas, eds, *The Greek Civil War*, Ashgate, London 2004

Carew, Anthony, *Labour Under the Marshall Plan*, Manchester University Press, Manchester 1987

Clay, Lucius, *Decision in Germany*, Doubleday, New York 1950

Cohen, Lizabeth, *A Consumers' Republic. The Politics of Mass Consumption in Postwar America*, Alfred A. Knopf, New York 2003

Copeland, Miles, *The Game of Nations*, Simon & Schuster, New York 1970

Dallek, Robert, *Franklin D. Roosevelt and American Foreign Policy*, Oxford University Press, New York 1979

Dalton, Hugh, *High Tide and After. Memoir 1945–1960*, Frederick Muller, London 1962
Dalton, Hugh, *The Political Diary of Hugh Dalton*, ed. Ben Pimlott, Jonathan Cape, London 1986
Dickie, John, *Special No More. Anglo-American Relations. Rhetoric and Reality*, Weidenfeld & Nicolson, London 1994
Dobney, Frederick, ed., *Selected Papers of Will Clayton*, Johns Hopkins University Press, Baltimore, 1971
Donovan, Robert J., *Conflict and Crisis. The Presidency of Harry S. Truman*, University of Missouri Press, Columbia, MO 1947
Duff Cooper, Alfred, *Old Men Forget. The Autobiography of Alfred Duff Cooper*, Rupert Hart-Davis, London 1953
Edmonds, Robin, *Setting the Mould. The United States and Britain, 1945–50*, Clarendon Press, Oxford 1985
Flanner, Janet, *Paris Journal 1944–1965*, Atheneum, New York 1965
Forrestal, James, *The Forrestal Diaries*, ed. Walter Mills, Viking Press, New York 1951
Forster, Margaret, *The Diary of an Ordinary Woman*, Chatto & Windus, London 2003
Fossedal, Gregory, *Our Finest Hour. Will Clayton, the Marshall Plan, and the Triumph of Democracy*, Hoover Press, Stanford, CA 1993
Fromkin, David, *In the Time of the Americans*, Vintage, New York 1996
Galbraith, John Kenneth, *The World Economy Since the War*, Mandarin, London 1974
Gardner, Richard N., *Sterling–Dollar Diplomacy in Perspective*, Columbia University Press, New York 1992
Garfield, Simon, *Our Hidden Lives. The Everyday Diaries of a Forgotten Britain 1945–1948*, Ebury Press, London 2004
Garwood, Ellen Clayton, *Will Clayton. A Short Biography*, University of Texas Press, Austin 1958
Gimbel, John, *The Origins of the Marshall Plan*, Stanford University Press, Stanford, CA 1968
Goulden, Joseph, *The Best Years, 1945–1950*, Atheneum, New York 1976
Gowing, Margaret, *Independence and Deterrence. Britain and Atomic Energy, 1945–1952*, Macmillan, London (for the Atomic Energy Authority) 1974
Griffiths, Richard T., ed., *Explorations in OEEC History*, OECD Publications, Paris 1997
Grose, Peter, *Operation Rollback. America's Secret War Behind the Iron Curtain*, Houghton Mifflin, New York 2000
Hacker, Clifford, ed., *Monnet and the Americans*, Jean Monnet Council, Paris 1975
Hamby, Alonzo L., *Man of the People. A Life of Harry S. Truman*, Oxford University Press, New York 1995
Harris, Kenneth, *A Prime Minister Remembers*, Heinemann, London 1961
Harris, Kenneth, *Attlee*, Weidenfeld & Nicolson, London 1982
Hartman, Susan, *Truman and the 80th Congress*, University of Missouri Press, Columbia MO 1971
Hathaway, Robert M., *Ambiguous Partnership. Britain and America, 1944–47*, Columbia University Press, New York 1981

Henderson, Sir Nicholas, *The Origins of NATO*, Weidenfeld & Nicolson, London 1982
Hennessy, Peter, *Never Again. Britain 1945–51*, Jonathan Cape, London 1992
Heykal, Mohammed, *Cutting the Lion's Tail. Suez Through Egyptian Eyes*, André Deutsch, London 1986
Heykal, Mohammed, *Iran. The Untold Story*, Pantheon, New York 1992
Hoffman, Paul G., *Peace Can Be Won*, Doubleday, New York 1951
Hogan, Michael, *The Marshall Plan. America, Britain and the Recovery of Western Europe, 1947–52*, Cambridge University Press, Cambridge 1987
Hoopes, Townsend and Douglas Brinkley, *Driven Patriot. The Life and Times of James Forrestal*, Alfred A. Knopf, New York 1992
Hopkins, Michael F., *Oliver Franks and the Truman Administration*, Frank Cass, London 1989
Howard, Norman, *A New Dawn. The General Election of 1945*, Politico's, London 2005
Hutton, Graham, *We Too Can Prosper*, Allen & Unwin, London 1953
Ireland, Timothy P., *Creating the Entangling Alliance. The Origins of the North Atlantic Treaty Organization*, Aldwych Press, London 1981
Isaacson, Walter and Evan Thomas, *The Wise Men. Six Friends and the World They Made*, Simon & Schuster, New York, 1986
Jenkins, Roy, *Truman*, Collins, London 1986
Jones, Jack, *Union Man*, Collins, London 1996
Jones, Joseph M., *The Fifteen Weeks*, Viking Press, New York 1955
Jones, Peter, *America and the British Labour Party*, I. B. Tauris, London 1947
Kaiser, Robert G., *Cold Winter, Cold War*, Stein & Day, New York 1974
Kedward, Rod, *La Vie en Bleu. France and the French Since 1900*, Allen Lane, London 2005
Kennan, George F., *Memoirs 1925–1950*, Little, Brown, Boston 1967
Kindleberger, Charles, *Marshall Plan Days*, Allen & Unwin, Boston 1987
Kinzer, Stephen, *All the Shah's Men. An American Coup and the Roots of Middle East Terrorism*, Wiley, New York 2003
Kipping, Matthias and Ove Bjarnar, eds, *The Americanisation of European Business. The Marshall Plan and the Transfer of U.S. Management Models*, Routledge, London 1998
Kolko, Gabriel and Joyce Kolko, *The Limits of Power. The World and U.S. Foreign Policy, 1945-54*, Harper & Row, New York 1972
Krock, Arthur, *Memoirs. Sixty Years in the Firing Line*, Cassell, London 1969
Kuisel, Richard, *Seducing the French. Dilemmas of Americanisation*, University of California Press, Berkeley, CA 1943
Kyle, Keith, *Suez*, Weidenfeld & Nicolson, London 1991
Kynaston, David, *Austerity Britain 1945–1951*, Bloomsbury, London 2007
Lilienthal, David, *Journals. The Atomic Energy Years 1945–1950*, Harper & Row, New York 1964
Louis, W. Roger and Hedley Bull, eds, *The Special Relationship. Anglo-American Relations Since 1945*, Clarendon Press, New York 1986
Mallalieu, William C., *British Reconstruction and American Policy*, Scarecrow Press, New York 1956

Manchester, William, *The Glory and the Dream. A Narrative History of America 1932–1972*, Michael Joseph, London 1976
Marchetti, Victor and Marks, John D., *The CIA and the Cult of Intelligence*, Alfred A. Knopf, New York 1974
Mayers, David, *George Kennan and the Dilemmas of U.S. Foreign Policy*, Oxford University Press, New York 1988
Mayne, Richard, *The Recovery of Europe*, Weidenfeld & Nicolson, London, 1970
Mayne, Richard, *Postwar. The Dawn of Today's Europe*, Thames & Hudson, London 1983
Meyer, Cord, *Facing Reality*, Harper & Row, New York 1980
Mitford, Nancy, *The Letters of Nancy Mitford and Evelyn Waugh*, ed. Charlotte Mosley, Hodder & Stoughton, London 1996
Morgan, Kenneth, *Labour in Power 1945–51*, Clarendon Press, Oxford 1984
Nutting, Sir Anthony, *No End of a Lesson. The Story of Suez*, Constable, London 1967
O][Ballance, Edgar, *The Greek Civil War 1944–1949*, Praeger, New York 1966
Orwell, George, *Collected Essays, Journalism and Letters*, vol. 4, Secker & Warburg, London 1968
Ostrander, F. Taylor, 'The Marshall Plan and Early NATO Revisited', unpublished paper, 2006
Pelling, Henry, *Britain and the Marshall Plan*, Macmillan, London 1984
Pimlott, Ben, *Hugh Dalton*, Jonathan Cape, London 1985
Pisani, Sallie, *The CIA and the Marshall Plan*, University Press of Kansas, Lawrence, KS 1991
Pogue, Forrest C., *George C. Marshall. Statesman*, Viking Press, New York 1987
Pogue, Forrest C., *George C. Marshall. Interviews and Reminiscences*, George C. Marshall Foundation, Lexington, VA 1992
Price, Harry Bayard, *The Marshall Plan and Its Meaning*, Cornell University Press, Ithaca NY 1955
Robertson Alex J., *The Bleak Midwinter 1947*, Manchester University Press, Manchester 1987
Roosevelt, Kermit, *Countercoup. The Struggle for the Control of Iran*, McGraw Hill, New York 1979
Rostow, W. W., *The Division of Europe After World War Two*, University of Texas Press, Austin 1982
Rothwell, Victor, *Britain and the Cold War, 1941–1947*, Jonathan Cape, London 1982
Sherwin, Martin, *A World Destroyed*, Alfred A. Knopf, New York 1975
Sissons, Michael and Philip French, eds, *The Age of Austerity*, Hodder & Stoughton, London 1963
Smith, Richard Harris, *OSS. The Secret History of America's First Intelligence Agency*, University of California Press, Berkeley 1972
Steel, Ronald, *Imperialists and Other Heroes. A Chronicle of the American Empire*, Random House, New York 1971
Strang, William, *Home and Abroad*, André Deutsch, London 1956
Sulzberger, C. L., *A Long Row of Candles*, Macmillan, New York 1959

Thompson, Alan, *The Day Before Yesterday*, Sidgwick & Jackson, London 1971
Thompson, E. P., *The Heavy Dancers*, Merlin, London 1985
Thorne, Christopher, *Allies of a Kind. The United States, Britain and the War Against Japan 1941–1945*, Oxford University Press, New York 1979
Truman, Harry S., *Memoirs*, Da Capo Press, New York 1955
Tusa, Ann and John Tusa, *The Berlin Airlift*, Atheneum, New York 1988
Vandenberg, Arthur H., ed., *The Private Papers of Senator Vandenberg*, Houghton Mifflin, New York 1952
van der Beugel, Ernst, *From Marshall Aid to Atlantic Partnership*, Elsevier, Amsterdam 1966
Walker, Martin, *The Cold War and the Origins of the Modern World*, Fourth Estate, London 1993
Wall, Irwin M., *The United States and the Making of Postwar France*, Cambridge University Press, Cambridge 1994
Waugh, Evelyn, *The Diaries of Evelyn Waugh*, ed. Michael Davies, Weidenfeld & Nicolson, London 1976
Weight, Robert, *Patriots. National Identity in Britain 1940–2000*, Pan Books, London 2002
Wheeler-Bennett, John, *King George VI. His Life and Reign*, Macmillan, London 1964
White, Theodore, *Fire in the Ashes. Europe in Mid-Century*, Sloane, New York 1953
Williams, William Appleman, *The Tragedy of American Diplomacy*, W. W. Norton, New York 1972
Wilson, Edmund, *Europe Without Baedeker*, Secker & Warburg, London 1948
Winks, Robin, *Cloak and Gown. Scholars in the Secret War 1939–61*, Yale University Press, New Haven 1986
Woodhouse, C. M., *Apple of Discord. Recent Greek Politics in Their International Setting*, Hutchinson, London 1948
Woodhouse, C. M., *Something Ventured*, Granada, London 1982
Xyldis, Stephen, *Greece and the Great Powers 1944–1947*, Institute for Balkan Studies, Thessaloniki 1963
Yergin, Daniel, *Shattered Peace. The Origins of the Cold War and the National Security State*, Houghton Mifflin, Boston 1977

INDEX